*SOME*
*REFLECTIONS*
*UPON*
*MARRIAGE*

SOME

# REFLECTIONS

UPON

# MARRIAGE

BY

MARY ASTELL

Source Book Press

Library of Congress Catalogue Card No. 70-134178

ISBN 0-87681-056-3

SOURCE BOOK PRESS, a Division of COLLECTORS EDITIONS LTD., 185 Madison Avenue, New York, N.Y. 10016

Unabridged republication of the 1730 London edition: First printing 1970

Corrections indicated in the "Errata" of the original have been made.

Type for this edition has been newly set.

Manufactured in the United States of America

SOME

# REFLECTIONS

UPON

# MARRIAGE.

With ADDITIONS.

The FOURTH EDITION.

*LONDON:*

Printed for WILLIAM PARKER, at the
*King's Head* in *St. Paul's* Church-Yard.

M.DCC.XXX.

# ADVERTISEMENT

THESE *Reflections being made in the Country, where the Book that occasion'd them came but late to Hand, the* Reader *is desir'd to excuse their Unseasonableness as well as other Faults; and to believe, that they have no other Design than to Correct some Abuses, which are not the less because Power and Prescription seem to authorize them. If any is so needlessly curious as to inquire from what Hand they come, they may please to know, that it is not good Manners to ask, since the Title Page does not tell them:* We are all of us sufficiently *Vain, and without doubt, the celebrated Name of* Author, *which most are so fond of, had not been avoided but for very good Reasons: To name but one;* Who will care to pull upon themselves an Hornet's Nest? *'Tis a very great Fault, to regard rather* Who *it is that speaks, than* What *is spoken; and either to submit to Authority, when we should only yield to Reason; or if Reason press too hard, to think to ward it off by Personal Objections and Reflections.* Bold *Truths may pass while the Speaker is* Incognito, *but are seldom endur'd when he is known; few Minds being* strong enough to bear what contradicts their Principles and Practices, without recriminating when they can. And though to tell the Truth be the most Friendly Office, yet whosoever is so hardy as to venture at it, shall be counted an Enemy for so doing.

The PREFACE in the last edition being extended to an uncommon Length, is now printed at the latter End, as an APPENDIX

# SOME
# REFLECTIONS
# UPON
# MARRIAGE

# SOME
# REFLECTIONS
# UPON
# MARRIAGE

CURIOSITY, which is sometimes an Occasion of Good, but more frequently of Mischief, by disturbing our own or our Neighbours Repose, having induc'd me to read the Account of an unhappy Marriage, I thought an Afternoon would not be quite thrown away in pursuing such *Reflections* as it occasion'd. I am far from designing a Satire upon Marriage, as some pretend, either unkindly or ignorantly, through want of *Reflection* in that Sense wherein I use the Word.

ONE wou'd have thought that Cardinal *Mazarine*, whose Dignity, Power and Riches, render'd him so considerable in the Eyes of all *Europe;* and who, like most great Ministers, aim'd at nothing so much as the aggrandizing himself and his Family, and who wanted no Opportunities of doing it, should have taken his Measures so justly as not to be disappointed: At least, that a Fabrick rais'd with so much Art and Cost, founded in the Oppression, and cemented with the Blood of the People, should not so quickly have tumbled into the Dust after him. But so it is, *Providence*, whether we think of it or no, overrules our Actions and baffles our best-concerted Projects: So that unless we wilfully shut our Eyes, we cannot but discern, that when *Men in* Power and *Honour* leave GOD out of their Schemes, they *have no Understanding*, though their natural Genius be ever so bright, *but are* justly *compared to the Beasts that perish.* The *Ignorant* and *Foolish* succeed quite as well as the *Worldly-wise*, who *carry nothing away with them when they* die, neither will their Riches and Glory descend as they intended. It is only by generous and worthy Actions that we are rescued from Oblivion, or from what is worse, being remembred with Contempt and Execrations: So little Reason is there to envy any Man's Wealth and Greatness, but much to emulate their Wisdom and Vertue whose Views extend to a more durable Felicity.

'TIS natural to well-turn'd Minds, when they hear of any Person eminent in Wit and Beauty, adorn'd with Politeness and Address, to wish these may be accompanied and supported by what is more valuable and lasting, solid Sense and real Vertue. One grieves at any Imputation on such an engaging Character, and if one cannot always find the favourite Person fortunate, one labours for the Consolation of finding them discreet; and even where their Conduct is not wholly blameless, Compassion and Good-nature will take Place of Censure in a Noble, as well as in a Christian Heart. We find out something to excuse, something to regret, lamenting that such a Treasure should fall into unworthy Hands, insensible of its Value, unskilful to preserve and improve it: We sigh, we grieve, that any Person capable of being an Ornament to a Family, and Blessing to the Age, should only serve as an unhappy Shipwreck to point out the Misfortune of an ill Education and unsuitable Marriage, and the inexpressible Danger of seeking Consolation and Relief, in any thing but Innocence and Vertue.

THEY only who have felt it, know the Misery of being forc'd to marry where they do not love; of being yok'd for Life to a disagreeable Person and imperious Temper, where Ignorance and Folly (the Ingredients of a Coxcomb, who is the most unsufferable Fool) tyrannizes over Wit and Sense: To be perpetually contradicted for Contradiction-sake, and bore down by Authority, not by Argument; to be denied one's most innocent Desires, for no other Reason but the absolute Will and Pleasure of a Lord and Master, whose Follies a Wife, with all her Prudence, cannot hide, and whose commands she cannot but despise at the same Time that she obeys them.

OR, suppose on the other Hand, she has married the Man she loves, heap'd upon him the highest

Obligations, by putting into his Power the Fortune he coveted, the Beauty he profess'd to adore; how soon are the Tables turn'd? It is her Part now to court and fawn; his real or pretended Passion soon cools into Indifference, Neglect, or perhaps Aversion. 'Tis well if he preserves a decent Civility, takes a little care of Appearances, and is willing to conceal his Breach of Faith.

But shall a Wife retaliate? God forbid! no Provocation, though ever so great, can excuse the Sin, or lessen the Folly: It were indeed a revenging the Injury upon herself in the most terrible Manner. The *Italian* Proverb shews a much better Way, *If you would be revenged of your Enemies, live well.*

Devotion is the proper Remedy, and the only infallible Relief in all Distresses; when this is neglected or turn'd into Ridicule, we run, as from one Wickedness, so from one Misfortune, to another. Unhappy is that Grandeur which is too great to be good, and that which sets us at a Distance from true Wisdom. Even Bigotry, as contemptible as it is, is preferable to profane Wit; for *that* requires our Pity, but *this* deserves our Abhorrence.

A Woman who seeks Consolation under Domestick Troubles from the Gaieties of a Court, from Gallantry, Gaming, rambling in Search of odd Adventures, childish, ridiculous and ill-natur'd Amusements, such as we find in the unhappy Madam

*M———'s Memoirs*, the common Methods of getting rid of Time, that is, of our very Being, and keeping as much as we can at a Distance from ourselves, will find these are very insignificant Applications; they hardly skin the Wound, and can never heal it, they even hurt, they make it fester, and render it almost incurable.

WHAT an ill Figure does a Woman make, with all the Charms of her Beauty, and Sprightliness of her Wit, with all her good Humour and insinuating Address, though she be the best Oeconomist in the World, the most entertaining Company, if she remit her Guard, abate in the Severity of her Caution, and Strictness of her Vertue? If she neglects those Methods which are necessary to keep her, not only from a Crime, but from the very Suspicion of one? She justifies the Injury her Husband has done her, by publishing to the World, that whatever good Qualities she may possess, Discretion, the Mistress of all the rest, is wanting: Though she be really guiltless, she cannot prove her Innocence, the Suspicions in her Prejudice are so strong. When she is censur'd, Charity, that thinks no Evil, can only be silent; though it believes and hopes the best, it cannot engage in her Defence, not apologize for irregular Actions.

AN ill Husband may deprive a Wife of the Comfort and Quiet of her Life, give occasion of exercising her Vertue, try her Patience and Fortitude to the utmost, which is all he can do; it is herself only that can accomplish her Ruin.

In vain we seek for Colours to varnish faulty Manners. An Advocate shews the best Side of his Wit, but the Worst of his Integrity when he has an ill Cause to manage: But to what Purpose? He cannot impose on the Judicious, his Colouring vanishes before their Eyes, and a good deal of Malice, with a very little Sense, will find the Weakness of his Arguments; so much more the suspected, by how much the more labour'd: For Truth is plain and forcible, depending on her own Strength; she requires no more than to be placed in a proper Light, nor condescends to Art or Insinuations, unless in Compassion to the Weakness and Prejudice of Mankind. Nor are they less mistaken in regard of Wit, which consists not meerly in saying what is odd and out of the way; Fools do this pretty often; but Wit consists in expressing good Sense in a surprising, yet natural and agreeable Manner.

There are some Reasons, (for the Laws of God and Man allow Divorces in certain Cases) though not many, that authorize a Wife's leaving her Husband, but if any Thing short of absolute Necessity, from irreclaimable Vice and Cruelty, prevails with her to break these sacred and strongest Bonds, how is she expos'd to Temptations and Injuries, Contempt, and the just Censure of the World. A Woman of

Sense, one shou'd think, could take but little pleasure in the Courtship and Flatteries of her Adorers, even when she is single: But for a married Woman to admit of Love Addresses, is worse than Folly; it is a Crime so ridiculous, that I will never believe a Woman of Sense can be guilty of it. For what does a Man pretend when he whines and dangles after a married Woman? Would he have her think he admires her, when he is treating her with the last Contempt? or that he loves her, when he is trying his Arts to gratify his brutal Passion, at the Price of all that is dear to her? His fine Speeches have either no Meaning, or a reproachful one; he affronts her Understanding as well as her Vertue, if he fancies she cannot discern, or wants Spirit to resent the Insults. She can look on him no otherwise than as the worst of Hypocrites, who flatters to betray, and fawns that he may ruin; who is laying Snares to entangle her in a Commerce founded on Injustice, and Breach of the most sacred Vows, carried on by Dissimulation, Treachery, Lyes, and Deceit, attended with Fear and Anxiety, Shame, Remorse, the bitter Stings of Guilt, whose fatal Consequences cannot be forseen, the least of which is the blasting of her Honour. And why all this Mischief? Why, because he professes to think her amiable, and with the blackest Treachery takes Advantage of her Weakness, and the too good Opinion she has entertained of him, to render her odious! to render her contemptible to himself, as well as to the World.

Who would be that unhappy Person with all her Grandeur, Wit, and Beauty, who gave Occasion to these *Reflections*? Who would live so infamously, and die so miserably? Whatever Apologies the Interested may invent, what they call Gallantry will find a harsher Name with the Modest and Discreet. Or else Gallantry, under whatever Form, must pass for a scandalous Amusement, not to be allow'd among Persons of Vertue and Honour. It is indeed ridiculous to talk of harmless Gallantry; there is, there can be no such Thing: For besides the Umbrage and Scandal, a Christian must be pure in Heart and Eyes; she who has vow'd her Affections to one, and is his Property, cannot without Injustice, and even Perjury, parcel them out to more.

It is in the Distempers of the Mind as in those of the Body, a little Care and Prudence will prevent what requires a long and difficult Regimen to cure: Therefore in both Cases the Aphorism holds; *Resist the Beginnings;* be early on your Guard. There was a Time when the most abandon'd Sinner would have shrunk with Horror, at what by Degrees becomes familiar, and, as they fancy, natural. The Sap is carry'd on against Vertue as artfully as against a fortified Town, and the Approaches are as methodical: But in this Case is different, the Besieged cannot fly; whereas Virtue is best secured by avoiding the Enemy. They are sensible of this, and therefore nothing more common than that silly Maxim, *That Vertue is not Vertue till it has been tried*. This is a Mortar-piece that has done more Execution than all their other Arts; for Self-confidence is always a Prelude to Destruction. The Wife who listens to Admirers runs into Temptation, and sports upon a Precipice. For, as a noble Lord, who knew the World perfectly well, instructs his Daughter, she may as well play with Fire, as dally with Gallantry. I can say nothing so well upon this Subject, as what is writ by this noble Author, whom therefore I beg leave to transcribe:

"The *Extravagancies* of the Age have made *Caution* more necessary; and by the same Reason that the too great License of ill Men, hath by Consequence in many Things restrained the lawful Liberty of those who did not abuse it, the unjustifiable Freedom of some of your Sex, have involved the rest in the Penalty of being reduced. And though this cannot so alter the Nature of Things, as to make that *Criminal*, which in it self is *Indifferent;* yet if it maketh it *dangerous,* that alone is sufficient to justify the *Restraint,* A *close Behaviour* is the fittest to receive *Vertue* for its constant *Guest,* because there, and there only, it can be secure. Proper *Reserves* are the Outworks, and must never be deserted by those who

13

intend to keep the Place; they keep off the Possibility not only of being *taken*, but of being *attempted;* and if a Woman seeth Danger at never so remote a Distance, she is for that Time to shorten her *Line* of *Liberty:* She who will allow herself to go to the *utmost Extents* of every thing that is *lawful*, is so very near going further, that those who lie at watch, will begin to count upon her.

MANKIND from the double Temptation of *Vanity* and *Desire*, is apt to turn every thing a *Woman* doth to the *hopeful Side;* and there are few who dare make an impudent Application, till they discern something which they are willing to take for an *Encouragement:* It is safer therefore to prevent such *Forwardness*, than to go about to *cure* it: It gathereth Strength by the first *Allowances*, and claimeth a Right from having been at any Time suffered with Impunity: Therefore nothing is with more Care to be avoided, than such a kind of *Civility* as may be mistaken for *Invitation.*"

IN the Time of Yore a *Knave* was no more than a Servant, and possibly a *Gallant* might originally denote a well-dress'd Coxcomb, who had nothing else to do but make Parade of his Wit and Cloaths, and perhaps of his Valour in Tournament, to gain the general Admiration of the Ladies, and the Honour of openly professing with Respect and Distance, his Veneration for some celebrated Beauty, or Woman of Merit. But modern Gallantry is quite a different Business: The Gallant, the fine Gentleman in Town, far superior to him upon the Road and all his Undergraduates, in carrying on his Plot, in the artful Contrivance of his Design, and Dexterity in executing it, happily combines the Cunning of the Fox, and the Audacity of the Tyger. Cruel indeed! for he tears the Fame, worries the Vertue, and compleats the Destruction of his unhappy Prey. 'Tis well for him that Christianity as yet prevails among us, for this obliges its Votaries to forgive the highest Injuries: Should the Morality of the honest Heathen, which some are pleas'd to profess, but not to practice, become the Fashion, or the old *English* Spirit, which has done and suffered so much for Liberty and Property, revive among us, alas! what would become of the *pretty Fellows*? Would they not run the Risque of being taken for Wolves, or Savages, have a Price set on their Heads, and be exterminated at any rate, that so among rational Persons we might be esteem'd a civiliz'd Nation?

These Destroyers avoided, and better Care taken than usual in Womens Education, Marriage might recover the Dignity and Felicity of its original Institution; and Men be very happy in a married State, if it be not their own Fault. The great Author of our Being, who does nothing in vain, ordained it as the only honourable Way of continuing our Race; as a Distinction between reasonable Creatures and meer Animals, into which we degrade our selves, by forsaking the Divine Institution. God ordained it for a Blessing, not a Curse: We are foolish as well as wicked, when that which was appointed for mutual Comfort and Assistance, has quite contrary Effect through our Folly and Perverseness. Marriage therefore, notwithstanding all the loose Talk of the Town, the Satires of antient, or modern Pretenders to Wit, will never lose its just Esteem from the Wise and Good.

THOUGH much may be said against this, or that Match; though the Ridiculousness of some, the Wickedness of others, and the Imprudence of too many, may provoke our Wonder, or Scorn, our Indignation or Pity; yet Marriage in general is too sacred to be treated with Disrespect, too venerable to be the Subject of Raillery and Buffoonery. None but the Impious will pretend to refine on a Divine Institution, or suppose there is a better Way for Society and Posterity. Whoever scoffs at this, and by odious Representation would possess the married Pair with a frightful Idea of each other, as if a Wife is nothing better than a Domestick Devil, an Evil he must tolerate for his own Conveniency; and an Husband must of necessity be a Tyrant or a Dupe; has ill Designs on both, and is himself a dangerous Enemy to the Publick, as well as to private Families.

BUT upon what are the Satires against Marriage grounded? Not upon the State it self, if they are just, but upon the ill Choice, or foolish Conduct of

those who are in it? and what has Marriage consider'd in it self to do with these? When the Blame
is laid where it ought to be, not Marriage, but in-
ordinate Passion, Rashness, Humour, Pride, Covetousness, Inconstancy, unjust Suspicions, unnecessary
Severity, and, in a Word, a silly, vicious, imprudent
Choice, or Conduct, ought to be arraign'd. For why
should Marriage be exclaim'd against when Men
reap the Fruit of their own Folly? If they will put
an unequal Yoke upon their own Necks, they have
their Choice, who can they blame for it? If instead
of a Help and Comfort, their Courtship has procured
them a Plague and Disgrace, who may they thank
but themselves: A Man can never be under any sort
of Obligation to marry against his Liking, but
through some reigning Vice, or want of Fortitude.

COULD there be no happy Marriages, Arguments
against Matrimony might have their Weight with
the Reasonable as well the Licentious. But since the
Laws of GOD and Man, founded upon Reason and
Experience, forbid a Temporary Contract, and engage the married Pair for Life, it is not only possible,
but highly probable, and not without many eminent
Instances, that there are and may be, happy Marriages; provided we act reasonably in our Choice and
Conduct, acquit ourselves like wise Men and Christians. So that all we have to say against Matrimony,
seems only to shew the Levity, or Impiety of our

own Minds: It is no more than a Flourish of Wit, and how prettily soever we may talk, it is but little to the Purpose.

Is it the being tied to *One* that offends us? Why this ought rather to recommend it to us, and would really do so, were we guided by Reason, and not by Humour or brutish Passion. He who does not make Friendship the chief Inducement to his Choice, and prefer it before any other Consideration, does not deserve a good Wife, and therefore should not complain if he goes without one. Now we can never grow weary of our Friends; the longer we have had them the more they are endear'd to us; and if we have One well assur'd, we need seek no farther, but are sufficiently happy in her. The Love of Variety in this and other Cases, shews only the ill Temper of our own Mind; for instead of being content with a competent Share of Good, thankfully and chearfully enjoying what is afforded us, and patiently bearing with the Inconveniencies that attend it, we would set up our Rest here, and expect Felicity where it is not to be found.

THE Christian Institution of Marriage provides the best that may be for Domestick Quiet and Content, and for the Education of Children; so that if we were not under the Tie of Religion, even the Good of Society and civil Duty, would oblige us to what Christianity requires: And since the very best of us are but poor frail Creatures, full of Ignorance and Infirmity, so that in Justice we ought to tolerate each other, and exercise that Patience towards our Companions to Day, which we shall give them occasion to shew towards us To-morrow; the more we are accustom'd to any one's Conversation, the better shall we understand their Humour, be more able to comply with their Weakness, and less offended at it. For he who would have every one submit to his Humours, and will not in his Turn comply with them, (though we should suppose him always in the right, whereas a Man of this Temper very seldom is so) is not fit for a Husband, scarce fit for Society, but ought to be turn'd out of the Herd as an unreasonable Creature.

THERE may indeed be Inconveniencies in a married Life; but is there any Condition without them? And he who lives single, that he may indulge Licentiousness and give up himself to the Conduct of wild and ungovern'd Desires, (or indeed out of any other Inducement, than the Glory of GOD and the Good of his Soul, through the Prospect he has of doing more Good, or because his Frame and Disposition of Mind are more fit for a single than a married Life) may rail as he pleases against Matrimony, but can never justify his own Conduct, nor clear it from the Imputation of Wickedness and Folly.

BUT if Marriage be such a blessed State, how

comes it, may you say, that there are so few happy Marriages? Now in answer to this, it is not to be wonder'd that so few succeed; we should rather be surpriz'd to find so many do, considering how imprudently Men engage, the Motives they act by, and the very strange Conduct they observe throughout.

For pray, what do Men propose to themselves in Marriage? What Qualifications do they look after in a Spouse? What will she bring? is the first Enquiry: How many Acres? Or how much ready Coin? Not that this is altogether an unnecessary Question, for Marriage without a Competency, that is, not only a bare Subsistence, but even a handsome and plentiful Provision, according to the Quality and Circumstances of the Parties, is no very comfortable Condition. They who marry for Love, as they call it, find Time enough to repent their rash, Folly, and are not long in being convinc'd, that whatever fine Speeches might be made in the heat of Passion, there could be no *real Kindness* between those who can agree to make each other miserable. But tho' an Estate is to be consider'd, it should not be the *Main*, much less the only Consideration; for Happiness does not depend on Wealth; That may be wanting, and too often is, where This abounds. He who marries himself to a Fortune only, must expect no other Satisfaction than that can bring him; but let not him say that Marriage, but that his own covetousness or prodigal Temper, has made him unhappy. What Joy has that Man in all his Plenty, who must either run from home to possess it, contrary to all the Rules of Justice, to the Laws of GOD and Man, nay, even in Opposition to good Nature and good Breeding too, which some Men make more Account of than of all the rest; or else be forc'd to share it with a Woman whose Person or Temper is disagreeable, whose Presence is sufficient to sour all his Enjoyments, so that if he has any Remains of Religion or good Manners, he must suffer the Uneasiness of a continual Watch, to force himself to a constrain'd Civility?

FEW Men have so much Goodness as to bring themselves to a Liking of what they loath'd, meerly because it is their Duty to like; on the contrary, when they marry with an Indifferency, to please their Friends or increase their Fortune, the Indifferency proceeds to an Aversion, and perhaps even the Kindness and Complaisance of the poor abus'd Wife, shall only serve to increase it. What follows then? There is no Content at home, so it is sought elsewhere, and the Fortune so unjustly got, is as carelessly squander'd; the Man takes a Loose, what should hinder him? He has all in his Hands, and Custom has almost taken off that small Restraint Reputation us'd to lay. The Wife finds too late what was the

Idol the Man adored, which her Vanity, perhaps, or it may be the Commands and Importunities of Relations, would not let her see before; and now he has got That into his Possession, she must make Court to him for a little sorry Alimony out of her own Estate. If Discretion and Piety prevail upon her Passions, she sits down quietly contented with her Lot, seeks no Consolation in the Multitude of Adorers, since he whom only she desir'd to please because it was her Duty to do so, will take no Delight in her Wit or Beauty: She follows no Diversion to allay her Grief, uses no Cordials to support her Spirit, that may sully her Vertue or bring a Cloud upon her Reputation; she makes no Appeals to the mis-judging Croud, hardly mentions her Misfortunes to her most intimate Acquaintance, nor lays a Load upon her Husband to ease herself; but would, if it were possible, conceal his Crimes, though her Prudence and Vertue give him a thousand Reproaches witout her Intention or Knowledge; and retiring from the World, she seeks a more solid Comfort than it can give her, taking Care to do nothing that Censoriousness, or even Malice it self can misconstrue to her Prejudice. Now she puts on all her Reserves, and thinks even innocent Liberties scarce allowable in her disconsolate State; she has other Business to mind: Nor does she in her Retirements reflect so much upon the Hand that administers this bitter Cup, as consider what is the best Use she can make of it. And thus indeed, Marriage, however unfortunate in other respects, becomes a very great Blessing to her. She might have been exposed to all the Temptations of a plentiful Fortune, have given up her self to Sloth and Luxury, and gone on at the common rate, even of the better Sort, in doing no hurt, and as little Good: But now her kind Husband obliges her to *Consider*, and gives Opportunity to exercise her Vertue; he makes it necessary to withdraw from those Gaieties and Pleasures of Life, which do more Mischief under the Shew of Innocency, than they could if they appear'd attended with a Crime, discomposing and dissolving the Mind, and making it uncapable of any manner of Good, to be sure of any thing Great and Excellent. Silence and Solitude, the being forc'd from the ordinary Entertainments of her Station, may perhaps seem a desolate Condition at first, and we may allow her, poor weak Woman! to be somewhat shock'd at it, since even a wise and courageous Man perhaps would not keep his Ground. We would conceal (if we could) for the Honour of the Sex, Mens being baffled and dispirited by a smaller matter, were not the Instances too frequent and too notorious.

But a little Time wears off all the Uneasiness, and puts her in possession of Pleasures, which till now she has unkindly been kept a Stranger to. Affliction, the sincerest Friend, the frankest Monitor, the best Instructor, and indeed, the only useful School that Women are ever put to, rouzes her Understanding, opens her Eyes, fixes her Attention, and diffuses such a Light, such a Joy into her Mind, as not only Informs her better, but Entertains her more than ever her *Ruel* did, though crouded by the Men of Wit. She now distinguishes between Truth and Appearances, between solid and apparent Good; has found out the Instability of all earthly Things, and won't any more be deceived by relying on them; can discern who are the Flatterers of her Fortune, and who the Admirers and Encouragers of her Vertue; accounting it no little Blessing to be rid of those Leeches, who hung upon her only for their own Advantage. Now sober Thoughts succeed to Hurry and Impertinence, to Forms and Ceremony; she can secure her Time, and knows how to improve it; never truly a happy Woman till she came, in the Eye of the World, to be reckon'd Miserable.

THUS the Husband's Vices may become an Occasion of the Wife's Vertues, and his Neglect do her a more real Good than his Kindness could. But all injur'd Wives don't behave themselves after this Fashion, nor can their Husbands justly expect it. With what Face can he blame her for following his Example, and being as extravagant on the one Hand, as he is on the other? Though she cannot justify her

Excesses to GOD, to the World, nor to her Self, yet surely in respect of him they may admit of an Excuse. For to all the rest of his Absurdities, (for Vice is always unreasonable) he adds one more, who expects that Vertue from another which he won't practice himself.

BUT suppose a Man does not marry for Money, though for one that does not, perhaps there are thousands that do; suppose he marries for Love, an Heroick Action, which makes a mighty Noise in the World, partly because of its Rarity, and partly in regard of its Extravagancy, what does his marrying for Love amount to? There's no great Odds between his marrying for the Love of Money, or for the Love of Beauty; the Man does not act according to Reason in either Case, but is govern'd by irregular Appetites. But he loves her Wit perhaps, and this, you'll say, is more Spiritual, more Refin'd: Not at all, if you examine it to the Bottom. For what is that which now a-days passes under the Name of Wit? A bitter and ill-natured Raillery, a pert Repartee, or a confident talking at all; and in such a multitude of Words, it's Odds if something or other does not pass that is surprizing, though every Thing that surprizes does not please; some Things being wonder'd at for their Ugliness, as well as others for their Beauty. True Wit, durst one venture to describe it, is quite another Thing; it consists in such a Sprightliness of Imagination, such a Reach and Turn of Thought, so properly express'd, as strikes and pleases a judicious Taste. For though, as one says of Beauty, *'tis in no Face, but in the Lover's Mind*, so it may be said of some sorts of Wit, it is not in him that speaks, but in the Imagination of his Hearer; yet doubtless there is a true Standard-Wit, which must be allow'd for such by every one who understands the Terms. I don't say that they shall all *equally* like it; and it is this Standard-wit that always pleases, the Spurious does so only for a Season.

Now what is it that strikes a judicious Taste? Not that, to be sure, which injures the Absent, or provokes the Company, which poisons the Mind under Pretence of entertaining it, proceeding from, or giving Countenance to false Notions, to dangerous and immoral Principles. Wit indeed is distinct from Judgment, but it is not contrary to it; 'tis rather its Handmaid, serving to awaken and fix the Attention, that so we may judge rightly. Whatever charms, does so because of its Regularity and Proportion; otherwise, though it is Extraordinary and out of the Way, it will only be star'd on like a Monster, but can never be lik'd. And tho' a Thought is ever so fine and new, ever so well express'd, if it suits not with Decorum and good Manners, it is not just and fit, and therefore offends our Reason, and consequently has no real Charms, nor would afford us any Entertainment, if our Taste were not deprav'd.

But it must not be suppos'd that Womens Wit approaches those Heights which Men arrive at, or that they indulge those Liberties the other take. Decency lays greater Restraints on them, their Timorousness does them this one, and perhaps this only Piece of Service, it keeps them from breaking through these Restraints, and following their Masters and Guides in many of their daring and masculine Crimes. As the World goes, your Witty Men are usually distinguish'd by the Liberty they take with Religion, good Manners, or their Neighbours Reputation: But, God be thank'd, it is not yet so bad, as that Women should form Cabals to propagate Atheism and Irreligion* A Man then cannot hope to find a Woman whose Wit is of a Size with his, but when he doats on Wit, it is to be imagin'd he makes Choice of that which comes the nearest to his own.

Thus, whether it be Wit or Beauty that a Man's in Love with, there are no great Hopes of a lasting Happiness; Beauty, with all the Helps of Art, is of no long Date; the more it is help'd, the sooner it decays; and he, who only or chiefly chose for Beauty, will in a little Time find the same Reason for another Choice. Nor is that sort of Wit which he

* This was wrote in the Beginning of the present Century.

27

prefers, of a more sure Tenure; or allowing it to last, it will not always please. For that which has not a real Excellency and Value in it self, entertains no longer than that giddy Humour which recommended it to us holds; and when we can like on no just, or on very little Ground, 'tis certain a Dislike will arise, as lightly and as unaccountably. And it is not improbable that such a Husband may in a little Time, by ill Usage, provoke such a Wife to exercise her Wit, that is, her Spleen on him, and then it is not hard to guess how very agreeable it will be to him.

In a word, when we have reckon'd up how many look no further than the making of their Fortune, as they call it; who don't so much as propose to themselves any Satisfaction in the Woman to whom they plight their Faith, seeking only to be Masters of her Estate, that so they may have Money enough to indulge all their irregular Appetites; who think they are as good as can be expected, if they are but, according to the fashionable Term, *Civil Husbands*; when we have taken the Number of your giddy Lovers, who are not more violent in their Passion than they are certain to repent of it; when to these you have added such as marry without any Thought at all, further than it is the Custom of the World, what others have done before them, that the Family must be kept up, the antient Race preserv'd, and therefore their kind Parents and Guardians choose as they think convenient, without ever consulting the Young one's Inclinations, who must be satisfied, or pretend so at least, upon Pain of their Displeasure, and that heavy Consequence of it, Forfeiture of their Estate: These set aside, I fear there will be but a small Remainder to marry out of better Considerations; and even amongst the Few that do, not one in a Hundred takes Care to deserve his Choice.

But do the Women never choose amiss? Are the Men only in Fault? That is not pretended; for he who will be just, must be forc'd to acknowledge, that neither Sex are always in the right. A Woman, indeed, can't properly be said to Choose; all that is allow'd her, is to Refuse or Accept what is offer'd. And when we have made such reasonable Allowances as are due to the Sex, perhaps they may not appear so much in Fault as one would at first imagine, and a generous Spirit will find more Occasion to Pity, than to Reprove. But sure I must transgress—it must not be suppos'd that the Ladies can do amiss! He is but an ill-bred Fellow who pretends that they need Amendment! They are, no doubt on't, always in the right, and most of all when they take Pity on distressed Lovers! Whatever they *say* carries an Authority that no Reason can resist, and all that they *do* must needs be Exemplary! This is the Modish Language, nor is there a Man of Honour amongst the whole Tribe, that would not venture his Life, nay, and his Salvation too, in their Defence, if any but himself attempts to injure them. But I must ask Pardon if I can't come up to these Heights, nor flatter them with the having no Faults, which is only a malicious Way of continuing and increasing their Mistakes.

WOMEN, it's true, ought to be treated with Civility; for since a little Ceremony and out-side Respect is all their Guard, all the Privelege that's allow'd them, it were barbarous to deprive them of it; and because I would treat them civilly, I would not express my Civility at the usual rate. I would not, under Pretence of Honouring and paying a mighty Deference to the Ladies, call them Fools, or what's worse, to their Faces; For what are all the fine Speeches and Submissions that are made, but an abusing them in a well-bred Way? She must be a Fool with a Witness, Who can believe a Man, Proud and Vain as he is, will lay his boasted Authority, the Dignity and Prerogative of his Sex, one Moment at her Feet, but in Prospect of taking it up again to more Advantage; he may call himself her Slave a few Days, but it is only in order to make her his all the rest of his Life.

INDEED that mistaken Self-Love that reigns in the most of us, both Men and Women, that over-good Opinion we have of ourselves, and Desire that others should have of us, makes us swallow every Thing that looks like Respect, without examining how wide it is from what it appears to be. For nothing is in Truth a greater Outrage than Flattery and feign'd Submissions; the plain *English* of which is this,

"I have a very mean Opinion both of your Understanding and Vertue; you are Weak enough to be impos'd on, and Vain enough to snatch at the Bait I throw; there's no Danger of your finding out my Meaning, or disappointing me of my Ends. I offer you *Incense*, 'tis true, but you are like to pay for't, and to make me a Recompense for your Folly, in imagining I would give my self this Trouble, did I not hope, nay, were I not sure, to find my own Account in it. If for nothing else, you'll serve at least as an Exercise of my Wit; and how much soever you swell with my Breath, 'tis I deserve the Praise for talking so well on such a poor Subject. We, who make the Idols, are the greater Deities; and as we set you up, so it is in our Power to reduce you to your first Obscurity, or to somewhat worse, to Contempt; you are therefore only on your good Behaviour, and are like to be no more than what we please to make you."

This is the Flatterer's Language aside, this is the true Sense of his Heart, whatever his Grimace may be before the Company.

AND if this be the true Meaning of honourable Courtship, what is meant by that Jargon, that Profusion of Love and Admiration which passes for Gallantry, when either of the Parties are married?

Is it not the utmost Scurrility, in that it supposes she is, or that he hopes to make her, what good Manners forbids to name? And since he makes so free with the Lady's Honour, can she afford him a civiller Answer, than what her Footman may deliver with a Crab-tree? But I correct my self,—this might be the Air of a haughty *Roman* Prude; our *British* Beauties are far more Gentle and Well-bred. And he who has the same Designs upon other Mens Relations, is sometimes so civil as to bear with the Outrages offer'd to his own.

Not but that 'tis possible, and sometimes Matter of Fact, to express our selves beyond the Truth in Praise of a Person, and yet not be guilty of Flattery; but then we must Think what we Say, and Mean what we Profess. We may be so blinded by some Passion or other, especially Love, which in Civil and Good-natur'd Persons is apt to exceed, as to believe some Persons more deserving than they really are, and to pay them greater Respect and Kindness than is in Strictness due to them. But this is not the present Case; for our fine Speech-makers doat too much on themselves to have any great Passion for another. Their Eyes are commonly too much fix'd on their own Excellencies, to view another's good Qualities through a Magnifying-Glass; at least if they ever turn that End of the Perspective towards their Neighbours, 'tis only in Respect and Reference to themselves. They are their own Centres, they find a Disproportion in every Line that does not tend thither, and in the next Visit they make, you shall hear all the fine Things they had said, repeated to the new Object, and nothing remembred of the former but her Vanity, or something else as ridiculous, which serves for a Foil, or a Whet to Discourse. For let there be ever so many Wits in the Company, Conversation would languish, and they would be at a Loss, did not a little Censoriousness come in at a Need to help them.

Let us then treat the Ladies as civilly as may be, but let us not do it by Flattering them, but by endeavouring to make them such as may truly deserve our hearty Esteem and Kindness. Men ought really for their own Sakes, to do what in them lies to make Women Wise and Good, and then it might be hoped they themselves would effectually Study and Practice that Wisdom and Vertue they recommend to others. But so long as Men, even the best of them, who do not outrage Women they pretend to adore, have base and unworthy Ends to serve, it is not to be expected that they should consent to such Methods as would certainly disappoint them. They would have their own Relations do well; it is their Interest: but it sometimes happens to be for their Turn that another Man's should not, and then their Generosity fails them, and no Man is apter to find Fault with another's dishonourable Actions, than he who is ready to do, or perhaps has done the same himself.

AND as Men have little Reason to expect Happiness when they marry only for the Love of Money, Wit, or Beauty, as has been already shewn, so much less can a Woman expect a tolerable Life, when she goes upon these Considerations. Let the Business be carried as prudently as it can be on the Woman's Side, a reasonable Man can't deny that she has by much the harder Bargain: because she puts herself entirely into her Husband's Power, and if the Matrimonial Yoke be grievous, neither Law nor Custom afford her that Redress which a Man obtains. He who has Sovereign Power does not value the Provocations of a Rebellious Subject; he knows how to subdue him with Ease, and will make himself obey'd: But Patience and Submission are the only Comforts that are left to a poor People, who groan under Tyranny, unless they are Strong enough to break the Yoke, to Depose and Abdicate, which, I doubt, would not be allow'd of here. For whatever may be said against Passive-Obedience in another Case, I suppose there's no Man but likes it very well in this; how much soever Arbitrary Power may be dislik'd on a Throne, not *Milton*, nor *B.H.*———, nor any of the Advocates of Resistance, would cry up Liberty to poor *Female Slaves*, or plead for the Lawfulness of Resisting a private Tyrany.

IF there be a Disagreeableness of Humours, this, in my Mind, is harder to be born than greater Faults, as being a continual Plague, and for the most Part incurable. Other Vices a Man may grow weary of, or may be convinced of the Evil of them, he may forsake them, or they him, but his Humour and Temper are seldom, if ever, put off. Ill-nature sticks to him from his Youth to his grey Hairs, and a Boy that's Humorous and Proud, makes a Peevish, Positive, and Insolent Old Man. Now if this be the Case, and the Husband be full of Himself, obstinately bent on his own Way, with or without Reason, if he be one who must be always Admir'd, always Humour'd, and yet scarce knows what will please him; if he has Prosperity enough to keep him from considering, and to furnish him with a Train of Flatterers and obsequious Admirers; and Learning and Sense enough to make him a Fop in Perfection; for a Man can never be a compleat Coxcomb, unless he has a considerable Share of these to value himself upon; What can the poor Woman do? The Husband is too Wise to be Advis'd, too Good to be Reform'd, she must follow all his Paces, and tread in all his unreasonable Steps, or there is no Peace, no Quiet for her; she must Obey with the greatest Exactness, 'tis in vain to expect any manner of Compliance on his Side, and the more she complies, the more she may: his fantastical Humours grow with her Desire to gratify them, for Age increases Opinionatry in some, as well as it does Experience in others. Of such sort of Folks as these it was that *Soloman* spake, when he said, *Seest thou a Man wise in his own Conceit, there is more hope of a Fool than of him;* That is, the profligate Sinner, such a one being always a Fool in *Solomon's* Language, is in a fairer Way of being convinc'd of his Folly, and brought to Reason, than the Proud, Conceited Man. That Man, indeed, can never be good at Heart, who is full of Himself and his own Endowments: Not that it is necessary, because it is not possible (humanly speaking) for one to be totally ignorant of his own good Qualities, I had almost said, he *ought* to have a modest Sense of 'em, otherwise he can't be duly thankful, nor make Use of them that is required, to the Glory of God, and the Good of Mankind; but he views them in a wrong Light, if he discerns any Thing that may exalt him above his Neighbours, make him over-look their Merit, or treat them with Neglect or Contempt. He ought to behold them with Fear and Trembling, as Talents which he has freely receiv'd, and for which he is highly Accountable, and therefore they should not excite his Pride, but his Care and Industry.

AND if Pride and Self-conceit keep a Man who

has some good Qualities, and is not so bad as the most of his Neighbours, from growing better, it for certain confirms and hardens the Wicked in his Crimes, it sets him up for a Wit, that is, according to modern Acceptation, one who rallies all that is serious, a Contemner of the Priests first, and then of the Deity Himself. For Penitence and Self-condemnation are what his Haughtiness cannot bear, and since his Crimes have brought upon him the Reproaches of his own Mind, since he will not take the regular Way to be rid of them, which is, by Humbling himself, and making his Peace with Heaven, he bids Defiance to it, and wou'd, if he could, believe there is no future State, no After-retribution, because he has too just Reason to fear it.

If therefore it be a Woman's hard Fate to meet with a disagreeable Temper, and of all others, the Haughty, Imperious, and Self-conceited are the most so, she is as unhappy as any Thing in this World can make her. For when a Wife's Temper does not please, if she makes her Husband uneasy, he can find Entertainments Abroad; he has a hundred Ways of relieving himself; but neither Prudence nor Duty will allow a Woman to fly out: her Business and Entertainment are at home; and tho' he makes it ever so uneasy to her, she must be content, and make her best on't. She who elects a Monarch for Life, who gives him an Authority, she cannot recall, however he misapply it, who puts her Fortune and Person entirely in his Power, nay, even the very Desires of her Heart, according to some learned Casuists, so as that it is not lawful to Will or Desire any Thing but what he approves and allows, had need be very sure that she does not make a Fool her Head, nor a Vicious Man her Guide and Pattern; she had best stay till she can meet with one who has the Government of his own Passions, and has duly regulated his own Desires, since he is to have such an absolute Power over hers. But he who doats on a Face, he who makes Money his Idol, he who is charm'd with vain and empty Wit, gives no such Evidence, either of Wisdom or Goodness, that a Woman of any tolerable Sense shou'd care to venture her self to his Conduct.

INDEED, your fine Gentleman's Actions are now a-days such, that did not Custom and the Dignity of his Sex give Weight and Authority to them, a Woman that thinks twice might bless her self, and say, Is this the Lord and Master to whom I am to promise Love, Honour and Obedience? What can be the Object of Love but amiable Qualities, the Image of the Deity impress'd upon a generous and godlike Mind, a Mind that is above this World, to be sure above all the Vices, the Tricks and Baseness of it; a Mind that is not full of it self, nor contracted to little private Interests, but which, in Imitation of that glorious Pattern it endeavours to copy after, expands and diffuses it self to its utmost Capacity in doing Good. But this fine Gentleman is quite of another Strain, he is the Reverse of this in every Instance. He is, I confess, very fond of his own Dear Person, he sees very much in it to admire; his Air and Mien, his Words and Actions, every Motion he makes, declare it; but they must have a Judgment of his Size, every whit as shallow, and a Partiality as great as his own, who can be of his Mind. How then can I Love? And if not Love, much less Honour. Love may arise from Pity, or a generous Desire to make that Lovely which as yet is not so, when we see any hopes of Success in our Endeavours of improving it; but Honour supposes some excellent Qualities already, something worth our Esteem; but, alas! there is nothing more contemptible than this Trifle of a Man, this meer Out-side, whose Mind is as base and mean as his external Pomp is glittering. His Office or Title apart, to which some ceremonious Observance must be paid for Order's sake, there's nothing in him that can command our Respect. Strip him of Equipage and Fortune, and such Things as only dazle our Eyes and Imaginations, but don't in any measure affect our Reason, or cause a Reverence in our Hearts, and the poor Creature sinks beneath our Notice, because not supported by real Worth. And if a Woman can neither Love nor Honour, she does ill in promising to Obey, since she is like to have a crooked Rule to regulate her Actions.

A MEER Obedience, such as is paid only to Authority, and not out of Love and a Sense of the Justice and Reasonableness of the Command, will be of an uncertain Tenure. As it can't but be uneasy to the Person who pays it, so he who receives it will be sometimes disappointed when he expects to find it: For that Woman must be endow'd with a Wisdom and Goodness much above what we suppose the Sex capable of, I fear much greater than any Man can pretend to, who can so constantly conquer her Passions, and divest her self even of Innocent Self-love, as to give up the Cause when she is in the Right, and to submit her inlightned Reason, to the imperious Dictates of a blind Will, and wild Imagination, even when she clearly perceives the ill Consequences of it, the Imprudence, nay, Folly and Madness of such a Conduct.

AND if a Woman runs such a Risque when she marries prudently, according to the Opinion of the World, that is, when she permits her self to be dispos'd of to a Man equal to her in Birth, Education and Fortune, and as good as the most of his Neighbours, (for if none were to marry, but Men of strict Vertue and Honour, I doubt the World would be but thinly Peopled) if at the very best her Lot is hard, what can she expect who is Sold, or any otherwise betray'd into mercenary Hands, to one who is in all, or most respects, unequal to her? A Lover who comes upon what is call'd equal Terms, makes no very advantageous Proposal to the Lady he courts, and to whom he seems to be an humble Servant. For under many sounding Compliments, Words that have nothing in them, this is his true Meaning; He wants one to manage his Family, an House-keeper, one whose Interest it will be not to wrong him, and in whom therefore he can put greater Confidence than in any he can hire for Money. One who may breed his Children, taking all the Care and Trouble of their Education, to preserve his Name and Family. One whose Beauty, Wit, or good Humour and agreeable Conversation, will entertain him at Home when he has been contradicted and disappointed Abroad; who will do him that Justice the ill-natur'd World denies him; that is, in any one's Language but his own, sooth his Pride and flatter his Vanity, by having always so much good Sense as to be on his Side, to conclude him in the Right, when others are so ignorant, or so rude, as to deny it. Who will not be blind to his Merit nor contradict his Will and Pleasure, but make it her Business, her very Ambition to content him; whose Softness and gentle Compliance will calm his Passions, to whom he may safely disclose his troublesome Thoughts, and in her Breast discharge his Cares; whose Duty, Submission and Observance, will heal those Wounds other Peoples Opposition or Neglect have given him. In a word, one whom he can intirely Govern, and consequently may form her to his Will and Liking, who must be his for Life, and therefore cannot quit his Service, let him treat her how he will.

And if this be what every Man expects, the Sum of his violent Love and Courtship, when it is put into Sense, and rendred Intelligible, to what a fine pass does she bring her self who purchases a Lord and Master, not only with her Money, but with what is of greater Value, at the Price of her Discretion! Who has not so much as that poor Excuse, Precedent and Example; or if she has, they are only such as all the World condemns? She will not find him less a Governor because she was once his Superior, on the contrary, the Scum of the People are most Tyrannical when they get the Power, and treat their Betters with the greatest Insolence. For, as the wise Man long since observ'd, A Servant when he Reigns, is one of those Things for which the Earth is disquieted, and which no body is able to bear.

It is the hardest Thing in the World for a Woman to know that a Man is not Mercenary, that he does not act on base and ungenerous Principles, even when he is her Equal, because being absolute Master, she and all the Grants he makes her are in his Power, and there have been but too many Instances of Husbands, that by wheedling, or threatening their Wives, by seeming Kindness, or cruel Usage, have persuaded or forc'd them out of what has been settled on them. So that the Woman has in Truth no Security but the Man's Honour and Good-nature, a Security that in this present Age no wise Person would venture much upon. A Man enters into Articles very readily before Marriage, and so he may, for he performs no more of them afterwards than he thinks fit. A Wife must never dispute with her Husband; his Reasons are now, no doubt on't, better than hers, whatever they were before; he is sure to persuade her out of her Agreement, and bring her, it must be suppos'd, *Willingly*, to give up what she did vainly hope to obtain, and what she thought had been made sure to her. And if she shews any Refractoriness, there are Ways enough to humble her; so that by Right or Wrong the Husband gains his Will. For Covenants between Husband and Wife, like Laws in an Arbitrary Government, are of little Force, the Will of the Sovereign is All in All. Thus it is in Matter of Fact, I will not answer for the Right of it; for if the Woman's Reasons, upon which those Agreements are grounded, are not just and good, why did he consent to them? Was it because there was no other Way to obtain his Suit, and with an Intention to annul them when it shall be in his Power? Where then is his Sincerity? But if her Reasons are good, where is his Justice in obliging her to quit them? He neither way acts like an equitable or honest Man.

But when a Woman marries unequally and beneath her self, there is almost Demonstration that the Man is sordid and unfair; that instead of loving her he only loves himself, trapans and ruins her to serve his own Ends. For if he had not a mighty Opinion of himself, (which Temper is like to make an admirable Husband) he would never imagine that his Person and good Qualities could make Compensation for all the Advantages she quits on his Account. If he had a real Esteem for her, or valued her Reputation, he would not expose it, nor have her Discretion call'd in Question for his sake; and if he truly lov'd her, he would not reduce her to Straits and a narrow Fortune, nor so much as lessen her way of Living to better his own. For since God has placed different Ranks in the World, put some in a higher, and some in a lower Station, for Order and Beauty's sake, and for many good Reasons; though it is both our Wisdom and Duty not only to submit with Patience, but to be thankful and well-satisfied, when by his Providence we are brought low, yet there is no manner of Reason for us to degrade our selves; on the contrary, much why we ought not. The better our Lot is in this World, and the more we have of it, the greater is our Leisure to prepare for the next; we have the more Opportunity to exercise that God-like Quality, to taste that Divine Pleasure, doing Good to the Bodies and Souls of those beneath us. Is it not then ill Manners to Heaven, and an irreligious Contempt of its Favours, for a Woman to slight that nobler Employment, to which it has assign'd her, and thrust her self down to a meaner Drudgery, to what is in the very literal Sense a caring for the Things of the World, a caring not only to Please, but to Maintain a Husband?

AND a Husband so chosen will not at all abate of his Authority and Right to Govern, whatever fair Promises he might make before. She has made him her Head, and he thinks himself as well qualified as the Best to act accordingly, nor has she given him any such Evidence of her Prudence as may dispose him to make an Act of Grace in her Favour. Besides, great Obligations are what Superiors cannot bear, they are more than can be return'd; to acknowledge were only to reproach themselves with Ingratitude, and therefore the readiest Way is, not to own, but overlook them, or rather, as too many do, to repay them with Affronts and Injuries.

WHAT then is to be done? How must a Man choose, and what Qualities must incline a Woman to accept, that so our married Couple may be as happy as that State can make them? This is no hard Question; let the Soul be principally consider'd, and

Regard had in the first place to a good Understanding, a vertuous Mind; and in all other respects let there be as much Equality as may be. If they are good Christians and of suitable Tempers all will be well; but I should be shrewdly tempted to suspect their Christianity who marry after any of those Ways we have been speaking of. I dare venture to say, that they don't act according to the Precepts of the Gospel, they neither shew the Wisdom of the Serpent, nor the Innocency of the Dove; they have neither so much Government of themselves, nor so much Charity for their Neighbours; they neither take such Care not to scandalize others, nor to avoid Temptations themselves, are neither so much above this World, nor so affected with the next, as they would certainly be, did the Christian Religion operate in their Hearts, did they rightly understand, and sincerely practise it, or acted *indeed* according to the Spirit of the Gospel.

BUT it is not enough to enter wisely into this State, Care must be taken of our Conduct afterwards. A Woman will not want being admonish'd of her Duty; the Custom of the World, Oeconomy, every Thing almost reminds her of it. Governors do not often suffer their Subjects to forget Obedience through their want of demanding it; perhaps Husbands are but too forward on this Occasion, and claim their Right oftner and more imperiously than either Discretion or good Manners will justify, and might have both a more chearful and constant Obedience paid them if they were not so rigorous in exacting it. For there is a mutual Stipulation, and Love, Honour, and Worship, by which certainly Civility and Respect at least are meant, are as much the Woman's Due, as Love, Honour and Obedience are the Man's. And being the Woman is said to be the weaker Vessel, the Man should be more careful not to grieve or offend her. Since her Reason is suppos'd to be less, and her Passions stronger than his, he should not give Occasion to call that Supposition in Question by his pettish Carriage and needless Provocations. Since he is the *Man*, by which very word Custom would have us understand not only greatest Strength of Body, but even greatest Firmness and Force of Mind, he should not play the *Little Master* so much as to expect to be cocker'd, nor run over to that Side which the Woman us'd to be rank'd in; for, according to the Wisdom of the *Italians, Will you? Is spoken to sick Folks.*

INDEED Subjection, according to the common Notion of it, is not over easy; none of us, whether Men or Women, but have so good an Opinion of our own Conduct, as to believe we are fit, if not to direct others, at least to govern our selves. Nothing but a sound Understanding, and Grace, the best Improver of Natural Reason, can correct this

Opinion, truly humble us, and heartily reconcile us to Obedience. This bitter Cup therefore ought to be sweetned as much as may be; for Authority may be preserv'd and Government kept inviolable, without that nauseous Ostentation of Power, which serves to no End or Purpose but to blow up the Pride and Vanity of those who have it, and to exasperate the Spirits of such as must truckle under it.

INSOLENCE is never the Effect of Power but in weak and cowardly Spirits, who wanting true *Merit* and Judgment to support themselves in that Advantageous Ground on which they stand, are ever appealing to their Authority, and making a Shew of it to maintain their Vanity and Pride. A truly great Mind, and such as is fit to Govern, tho' it may stand on its Right with its Equals, and modestly expect what is due to it even from its Superiors, yet it never contends with its Inferiors, nor makes use of its Superiority but to do them Good. So that considering the just Dignity of Man, his great Wisdom so conspicuous on all Occasions! the Goodness of his Temper, and Reasonableness of all his Commands, which make it a Woman's Interest as well as Duty to be observant and obedient in all Things; that his Prerogative is settled by an undoubted Right and the Prescription of many Ages; it cannot be suppos'd, that he should make frequent and insolent Claims of an Authority so well establish'd and us'd with such Moderation, nor give an impartial By-stander (could such an one be found) any Occasion from thence to suspect that he is inwardly conscious of the Badness of his Title; Usurpers being always most desirous of Recognitions, and busy in imposing Oaths, whereas a Lawful Prince contents himself with the usual Methods and Securities.

AND since Power does naturally puff up, and he who finds himself exalted, seldom fails to think he *ought* to be so, it is more suitable to a Man's Wisdom and Generosity, to be mindful of his great Obligations, than to insist on his Rights and Prerogatives. Sweetness of Temper and an obliging Carriage are so justly due to a Wife, that a Husband who must not be thought to want either Understanding to know what is fit, nor Goodness to perform it, can't be suppos'd not to shew them. For setting aside the Hazard of her Person to keep up his Name and Family, with all the Pains and Trouble that attend it, which may well be thought great enough to deserve all the Respect and Kindness that may be; setting this aside, though 'tis very considerable, a Woman has so much the Disadvantage in *most*, I was about to say, in *all* Things, that she makes a Man the greatest Compliment in the World when she condescends to take him *for Better for Worse*. She puts her self intirely in his Power, leaves all that is dear to her, her Friends and Family, to espouse his Interests and follow his Fortune, and makes it her Business and Duty to please him! What Acknowledgments, what Returns can he make? What Gratitude can be sufficient for such Obligations? She shews her good Opinion of him by the great Trust she reposes in him, and what a Brute must he be who betrays that Trust, or acts any way unworthy of it? Ingratitude is one of the basest Vices, and if a Man's Soul is sunk so low as to be guilty of it towards her who has so generously oblig'd him, and who so intirely depends on him, if he can treat her disrespectfully, who has so fully testified her Esteem of him, she must have a Stock of Vertue which he should blush to discern, if she can pay him that Obedience of which he is so unworthy.

Superiors indeed are too apt to forget the common Privileges of Mankind; that their Inferiors share with them the greatest Benefits, and are as capable as themselves of enjoying the supreme Good; that though the Order of the World requires an *Outward* Respect and Obedience from some to others, yet the Mind is free, nothing but Reason can oblige it, 'tis out of the Reach of the most absolute Tyrant. Nor will it ever be well either with those who Rule or those in Subjection, even from the Throne to every private Family, till those in Authority look on themselves as plac'd in that Station for the Good and Improvement of their Subjects, and not for their own Sakes; not as the Reward of their Merit, or that they may prosecute their own Desires and fulfil all their Pleasure, but as the Representatives of GOD, whom they ought to imitate in the Justice and Equity of their Laws, in doing Good and communicating Blessings to all beneath them: By which, and not by following the imperious Dictates of their own Will, they become truly Great and Illustrious, and worthily fill their Place. And the Governed for their Part, ceasing to envy the Pomp and Name of Authority should respect their Governors as placed in GOD'S stead, and contribute what they can to ease them of their real Cares, by a chearful and ready Compliance, with their good Endeavours, and by affording them the Pleasure of Success in such noble and generous Designs.

FOR, upon a due Estimate, Things are pretty equally divided; those in Subjection, as they have a less Glorious, so they have an easier Task and a less Account to give; Whereas he who Commands, has in a great measure the Faults of others to answer for as well as his own. 'Tis true, he has the Pleasure of doing more Good than a private Person can, and shall receive the Reward of it when Time shall be no more, in Compensation for the Hazards he runs, the Difficulties he at present encounters, and the large Account he is to make hereafter. Which Pleasure and Reward are highly desirable, and most worthy our Pursuit; but they are Motives which such as Usurp on their Governors, and make them uneasy in the due Discharge of their Duty, never propose. As for those other little Things that move their Envy and Ambition, they are of no Esteem with a just Considerer, nor will such as violently pursue, find their Account in them.

But how can a Man respect his Wife when he has a contemptible Opinion of her and her Sex? When from his own Elevation he looks down on them as void of Understanding, full of Ignorance and Passion, so that Folly and a Woman are equivalent Terms with him? Can he think there is any Gratitude due to her whose utmost Services he exacts as strict Duty? Because she was made to be a Slave to his Will, and has no higher End than to Serve and Obey him? Perhaps we arrogate too much to our selves, when we say this Material World was made for our Sakes: That its Glorious Maker has given us the Use of it is certain; but when we suppose any Thing to be made purely for our Sakes, because we have Dominion over it, we draw a false Conclusion. As he who should say the People were made for the Prince who is set over them, would be thought to be out of his Senses as well as his Politicks. Yet even allowing that God, who made every Thing in Number, Weight and Measure, who never acts but for some great and glorious End, an

End agreeable to His Majesty; allowing that He created such a Number of Rational Spirits merely to serve their Fellow Creatures, yet how are these Lords and Masters help'd by the Contempt they shew of their poor humble Vassals? Is it not rather an Hindrance to that Service they expect, as being an undeniable and constant Proof how unworthy they are to receive it?

NONE of GOD's Creatures, absolutely consider'd, are in their own Nature contemptible; the meanest Fly, the poorest Insect has its Use and Vertue. Contempt is scarce a Human Passion, one may venture to say it was not in innocent Man, for till Sin came into the World, there was nothing in it to be contemn'd. But Pride, which makes every Thing serve its Purposes, wrested this Passion from its only Use, so that instead of being an Antidote against Sin, it is become a grand Promoter of it, nothing making us more worthy of that Contempt we shew, than when, poor, weak, dependent Creatures as we are! we look down with Scorn and Disdain on others.

THERE is not a surer Sign of a noble Mind, a Mind very far advanc'd towards Perfection, than the being able to bear Contempt and an unjust Treatment from one's Superiors evenly and patiently. For inward Worth and real Excellency are the true Ground of Superiority, and one Person is not in reality better than another, but as he is more Wise and Good. But this World being a Place of Trial, and govern'd by general Laws, just Retributions being reserv'd for hereafter, Respect and Obedience many times become due for Order's sake, to those who don't otherwise deserve them. Now tho' Humility keeps us from over-valuing our selves or viewing our Merit through a false and magnifying *Medium*, yet it does not put out our Eyes, it does not, it ought not to deprive us of that pleasing Sentiment which attends our Acting as we ought to Act, which is, as it were, a Foretaste of Heaven, our present Reward for doing what is just and fit. And when a Superior does a mean and unjust thing, as all Contempt of one's Neighbour is, and yet this does not provoke his Inferiors to refuse that Observance which their Stations in the World require, they cannot but have an inward Sense of their own real Superiority, the other having no Pretence to it, at the same Time that they pay him an outward Respect and Deference, which is such a flagrant Testimony of the sincerest Love of Order, as proves their Souls to be of the highest and noblest Rank.

A MAN therefore for his own sake, and to give Evidence that he has a Right to those Prerogatives he assumes, should treat Women with a little more Humanity and Regard than is usually paid them. Your whifling Wits may scoff at them, and what then? It matters not, for they rally every Thing though ever so sacred, and rail at the Women commonly in very good Company. Religion, its Priests, and those its most constant and regular Professors, are the usual Subjects of their manly, mannerly and surprizing Jests. Surprizing indeed! not for the Newness of the Thought, the Brightness of the Fancy, or Nobleness of Expression, but for the good Assurance with which such Thread-bare Jests are again and again repeated. But that your grave Dons, your learned Men, and, which is more, your Men of Sense, as they would be thought, should stoop so low as to make Invectives against the Women, forget themselves so much as to jest with their Slaves, who have neither Liberty, nor Ingenuity to make Reprizals; that they should waste their Time, and debase their good Sense, which fits them for the most weighty Affairs, such as are suitable to their profound Wisdom and exalted Understandings! to render those poor Wretches more ridiculous and odious who are already in their Opinion sufficiently contemptible, and find no better Exercise of their Wit and Satire, than such as are not worth their Pains, though it were possible to Reform them, this, this indeed may justly be wondred at!

I Know not whether or no Women are allow'd to have Souls; if they have, perhaps it is not prudent to provoke them too much, lest, silly as they are, they at last recriminate, and then what polite and well-bred Gentleman, though himself is concern'd, can forbear taking that lawful Pleasure, which all who understand Raillery must taste, when they find his Jests who insolently began to peck at his Neighbour, return'd with Interest upon his own Head? And indeed Men are too Humane, too Wise, to venture at it, did they not hope for this Effect, and expect the Pleasure of finding their Wit turn to such Account: For if it be lawful to pry into a Secret, this is, without doubt, the whole Design of those fine Discourses which have been made against the Women from our great Fore-Fathers to this present Time! Generous Man has too much Bravery, he is too Just and too Good to assault a defenceless Enemy, and if he did inveigh against the Women, it was only to do them Service! For since neither his Care of their Education, his hearty Endeavours to improve their Minds, his wholesome Precepts, nor great Example could do them good, as his last and kindest Essay, he resolv'd to try what Contempt would do, and chose rather to expose himself by a seeming Want of Justice, Equity, Ingenuity and Good-nature, than suffer Women to remain such vain and insigificant Creatures as they have hitherto been reckon'd; and truly, Women are some Degrees beneath what I have thus far thought them, if they do not make the best Use of his Kindness, improve themselves, and, like Christians, return it.

LET us see then what is their Part, what must they do to make the Matrimonial Yoke tolerable to themselves as well as pleasing to their Lords and Masters? That the World is an empty and deceitful Thing, that those Enjoyments which appear'd so desirable at a Distance, which rais'd our Hopes and Expectations to such a mighty Pitch, which we so passionately coveted, and so eargerly pursued, vanish at our first Approach, leaving nothing behind them but the Folly of Delusion, and the Pain of disappointed Hopes, is a common Outcry; and yet, as common as it is, though we complain of being deceiv'd this Instant, we do not fail of contributing to the Cheat the very next. Though in reality it is not the World that abuses us, 'tis we abuse our selves; it is not the Emptiness of That, but our own false Judgments, our unreasonable Desires and Expectations that torment us; for he who exerts his whole Strength to lift a Straw, ought not to complain of the Burden, but of his own disproportionate Endeavour which gives him the Pain he feels. The World affords us all the Pleasure a sound Judgment can expect from it, and answers all those Ends and Purposes for which it was design'd; let us expect no more than is reasonable, and then we shall not fail of our Expectations.

IT is even so in the Case before us; a Woman who has been taught to think Marriage her only Preferment, the Sum-Total of her Endeavours, the Completion of all her Hopes, that which must settle and make her Happy in this World, and very few, in their Youth especially, carry a Thought steadily to a greater Distance; She who has seen a Lover dying at her Feet, and can't therefore imagine that he who professes to receive all his Happiness from her, can have any other Design or Desire than to please her; whose Eyes have been dazled with all the Glitter and Pomp of a Wedding, and, who hears of nothing but Joy and Congratulation; who is transported with the Pleasure of being out of Pupillage, and Mistress not only of her self, but of a Family too: She who is either so simple or so vain, as to take her Lover at his Word, either as to the Praises he gave her, or the Promises he made for himself; in sum, she whose Expectation has been rais'd by Courtship, by all the fine Things that her Lover, her Governess and Domestick Flatterers say, will find a terrible Disappointment when the Hurry is over, and when she comes calmly to consider her Condition, and views it no more under a false Appearance, but as it truly is.

I Doubt in such a View it will not appear over-desirable, if she regards only the present State of Things. Hereafter may make amends for what she must be prepar'd to suffer here, then will be her Reward, this is her Time of Trial, the Season of exercising and improving her Vertues. A Woman that is not Mistress of her Passions, that cannot patiently submit, even when Reason suffers with her, who does not practise Passive Obedience to the utmost, will never be acceptable to such an absolute Sovereign as a Husband. Wisdom ought to Govern without Contradiction, but Strength however will be obeyed. There are but few of those wise Persons who can be content to be made yet wiser by Contradiction; the most will have their *Will*, and it is right because it is theirs. Such is the Vanity of Human Nature, that nothing pleases like an intire Subjection; what Imperfections won't a Man over-look where this is not wanting! Though we live like Brutes, we would have Incense offer'd us, that is only due to Heaven it self, would have an absolute and blind Obedience paid us by all over whom we pretend Authority. We were not made to Idolize one another, yet the whole Strain of Courtship is little less than rank Idolatry: But does a Man intend to give, and not to receive his Share in this Religious Worship? No such matter; Pride and Vanity, and Self-love have their Designs, and if the Lover is so condescending as to set a Pattern in the Time of his Addresses, he is so just as to expect his Wife should strictly Copy after it all the rest of her Life.

BUT how can a Woman scruple intire Subjection, how can she forbear to admire the Worth and Excellency of the Superior Sex, if she at all considers it! Have not all the great Actions that have been perform'd in the World been done by Men? Have not they founded Empires and over-turn'd them? Do not they make Laws and continually repeal and amend them? Their vast Minds lay Kingdoms waste, no Bounds or Measures can be prescrib'd to their Desires. War and Peace depend on them; they form Cabals and have the Wisdom and Courage to get over all the Rubs, the petty Restraints which Honour and Conscience may lay in the way of their desired Grandeur. What is it they cannot do? They make Worlds and ruin them, form Systems of universal Nature, and dispute eternally about them; their Pen gives Worth to the most trifling Controversy; nor can a Fray be inconsiderable if they have drawn their Swords in't. All that the wise Man pronounces is an Oracle, and every Word the Witty speaks, a Jest. It is a Woman's Happiness to hear, admire and praise them, especially if a little Ill-nature keeps them at any time from bestowing due Applauses on each other! And if she aspires no further, she is thought to be in her proper Sphere of Action; she is as wise and as good as can be expected from her!

SHE then who Marries, ought to lay it down for an indisputable Maxim, that her Husband must govern absolutely and intirely, and that she has nothing else to do but to Please and Obey. She must not attempt to divide his Authority, or so much as dispute it; to struggle with her Yoke will only make it gall the more, but must believe him Wise and Good, and in all respects the best, at least he must be so to her. She who can't do this is no way fit to be a Wife, she may set up for that peculiar Coronet the antient Fathers talk'd of, but is not qualified to receive that great Reward which attends the eminent Exercise of Humility and Self-denial, Patience and Resignation, the Duties that a Wife is call'd to.

BUT some refractory Woman perhaps will say, how can this be? Is it possible for her to believe him Wise and Good, who by a thousand Demonstrations convinces her, and all the World, of the contrary? Did the bare Name of Husband confer Sense on a Man, and the meer being in Authority infallibly qualify him for Government, much might be done. But since a wise Man and a Husband are not Terms convertible, and how loth soever one is to own it, Matter of Fact won't allow us to deny, that the Head many times stands in need of the Inferior's Brains to manage it, she must beg leave to be excus'd from such high Thoughts of her Sovereign, and if she submits to his Power, it is not so much Reason as Necessity that compels her.

Now of how little Force soever this Objection may be in other respects, me-thinks it is strong enough to prove the Necessity of a good Education, and that Men never mistake their true Interest more than when they endeavour to keep Women in Ignorance. Could they indeed deprive them of their Natural good Sense at the same Time they deny them the true Improvement of it, they might compass their End; otherwise Natural Sense unassisted may run into a false Track, and serve only to punish him justly, who would not allow it to be useful to himself or others. If Man's Authority be justly establish'd, the more Sense a Woman has, the more Reason she will find to submit to it; if according to the Tradition of our Fathers, (who having had *Possession* of the Pen, thought they had also the best *Right* to it) Womens Understanding is but small, and Man's Partiality adds no Weight to the Observation, ought not the more Care to be taken to improve them? How it agrees with the Justice of Men we inquire not, but certainly Heaven is abundantly more Equitable than to injoin Women the hardest Task, and give them the least Strength to perform it. And if Men, learned, wise and discreet as they are, who have, as is said, all the Advantages of Nature, and without Controversy have, or may have, all the Assistance of Art, are so far from acquitting themselves as they ought, from living according to that Reason and excellent Understanding they so much boast of, can it be expected that a Woman who is reckon'd silly enough in her self, at least comparatively, and whom Men take care to make yet more so; can it be expected that she should constantly perform so difficult a Duty as intire Subjection, to which corrupt Nature is so averse?

If the great and wise *Cato*, a *Man*, a Man of no ordinary Firmness and Strength of Mind, a Man who was esteem'd as an Oracle, and by the Philosophers and great Men of his Nation equal'd even to the Gods themselves; If he, with all his Stoical Principles, was not able to bear the Sight of a triumphant Conqueror, (who perhaps would have insulted, and perhaps would not) but out of a Cowardly Fear of an Insult, ran to Death, to secure him from it; can it be thought that an ignorant weak Woman should have Patience to bear a continual Outrage and Insolence all the Days of her Life? Unless you will suppose her a *very Ass*, but then remember what the *Italians* say, to quote them once more, since being *very* Husbands they may be presum'd to have some Authority in this Case, *An Ass, though slow, if provok'd, will kick.*

We never observe, or perhaps make Sport, with the ill Effects of a bad Education, till it comes to touch us home in the ill Conduct of a Sister, a Daughter, or Wife. Then the Women must be blam'd, their Folly is exclaim'd against, when all this while it was the wise Man's Fault, who did not set a better Guard on those, who, according to him, stand in so much need of one. A young Gentleman, as a celebrated Author tells us, ought above all Things to be acquainted with the State of the World, the Ways and Humours, the Follies, the Cheats, the Faults of the Age he is fallen into; he should by degrees by inform'd of the Vice in Fashion, and warn'd of the Application and Design of those who will make it their Business to corrupt him, should be told the Arts they use, and the Trains they lay, be prepar'd to be Shock'd by some, and Caress'd by others; warn'd who are like to oppose, who to mislead, who to undermine, and who to serve him. He should be instructed how to know and distinguish them, where he should let them see, and when dissemble the Knowledge of them and their Aims and Workings. Our Author is much in the right, and not to disparage any other Accomplishments which are useful in their Kind, this will turn to more Account than any Language or Philosophy, Art or Science, or any other Piece of Good-breeding and fine Education that can be taught him, which are no otherwise excellent than as they contribute to this, as this does above all Things to the making him a wise, a vertuous and useful Man.

AND it is not less necessary that a young Lady should receive the like Instructions, whether or no her Temptations be fewer, her Reputation and Honour however are to be more nicely preserv'd;

they may be ruin'd by a little Ignorance or Indiscretion, and then though she has kept her Innocence, and so is secur'd as to the next World, yet she is in a great measure lost to this. A Woman cannot be too watchful, too apprehensive of her Danger, nor keep at too great a Distance from it, since Man, whose Wisdom and Ingenuity is so much Superior to hers! condescends for his Interest sometimes, and sometimes by way of Diversion, to lay Snares for her. For though all Men are *Virtuosi,* Philosophers and Politicians, in comparison of the ignorant and illiterate Women, yet they don't all pretend to be Saints, and 'tis no great Matter to them, if Women, who were born to be their Slaves, be now and then ruin'd for their Entertainment.

But according to the rate that young Women are Educated, according to the Way their Time is spent, they are destin'd to Folly and Impertinence, to say no worse, and, which is yet more inhuman, they are blam'd for that ill Conduct they are not suffer'd to avoid, and reproach'd for those Faults they are in a Manner forc'd into; so that if Heaven has bestowed any Sense on them, no other Use is made of it, than to leave them without Excuse. So much, and no more, of the World is shewn them, than serves to weaken and corrupt their Minds, to give them wrong Notions, and busy them in mean Pursuits; to disturb, not to regulate their Passions; to make them timorous and dependant, and, in a Word, fit for nothing else but to act a Farce for the Diversion of their Governors.

EVEN Men themselves improve no otherwise than according to the Aim they take, and the End they propose; and he whose Designs are but little and mean, will be the same himself. Tho' Ambition, as 'tis usually understood, is a foolish, not to say a base and pitiful Vice, yet the Aspirings of the Soul after true Glory are so much its Nature, that it seems to have forgot it self, and to degenerate, if it can forbear; and perhaps the great Secret of Education lies in affecting the Soul with a lively Sense of what is truly its Perfection, and exciting the most ardent Desires after it.

BUT, alas! what poor Woman is ever taught that she should have a higher Design than to get her a Husband? Heaven will fall in of course; and if she makes but an Obedient and Dutiful Wife, she cannot miss of it. A Husband indeed is thought by both Sexes so very valuable, that scarce a Man who can keep himself clean and make a Bow, but thinks he is good enough to pretend to any Woman; no matter for the Difference of Birth or Fortune, a Husband is such a Wonder-working Name as to make an Equality, or something more, whenever it is obtain'd.

AND indeed, were there no other Proof of Masculine Wisdom, and what a much greater Portion of

Ingenuity falls to the Men than to the Women's Share, the Address, the Artifice, and Management of an humble Servant were a sufficient Demonstration. What good Conduct does he shew! what Patience exercise! what Subtilty leave untry'd! what Concealment of his Faults! what Parade of his Vertues! what Government of his Passions! How deep is his Policy in laying his Designs at so great a Distance, and working them up by such little Accidents! How indefatigable is his Industry, and how constant his Watchfulness not to slip any Opportunity that may in the least contribute to his Design! What a handsome Set of Disguises and Pretences is he always furnish'd with! How conceal'd does he lie! how little pretend, till he is sure that his Plot will take! And at the same Time that he nourishes the Hope of being Lord and Master, appears with all the Modesty and Submission of an humble and unpretending Admirer!

Can a Woman then be too much upon her Guard? Can her Prudence and Foresight, her early Caution, be reckon'd unnecessary Suspicion, or ill-bred Reserve by any but those whose Designs they prevent, and whose Interest it is to declaim against them? It being a certain Maxim with the Men, though Policy or good Breeding won't allow them to avow it always, that the Women were made for their Sakes and Service, and are in all respects their

Inferiors, especially in Understanding; so that all the Compliments they make, all the Address and Complaisance they use, all the Kindness they profess, all the Service they pretend to pay, has no other Meaning, no other End, than to get the poor Woman into their Power, to govern her according to their Discretion. This is all pure Kindness indeed, and therefore no Woman has Reason to be offended with it; for, considering how much she is expos'd in her own, and how safe in their Keeping, 'tis the wisest Thing she can do to put her self under Protection! And then if they have a tolerable Opinion of her Sense, and not their Vanity, but some better Principle disposes them to do something out of the Way, and to appear more generous than the rest of their Sex, they'll condescend to dictate to her, and impart some of their Prerogative, Books and Learning. 'Tis fit indeed, that she should intirely depend on their Choice, and walk with the Crutches they are pleas'd to lend her; and if she is furnished out with some Notions to set her a prating, I should have said, to make her entertaining, and the Fiddle of the Company, her Tutor's Time was not ill bestowed: And it were a diverting Scene to see her stript, like the Jay, of her borrowed Feathers, but he, good Man, has not ill Nature enough to take Pleasure in it. You may accuse him, perhaps, for giving so much Encouragement to a Woman's Vanity, but your Accusation is groundless, Vanity being a Disease the Sex will always be guilty of; nor is it a Reproach to them, since Men of Learning and Sense are over-run with it.

BUT there are few Women whose Understandings are worth the Management, their Estates are much more capable of Improvement. No Woman, much less a Woman of Fortune, is ever fit to be her own Mistress, and he who has not the Vanity to think what much finer Things he could perform, had he the Management of her Fortune; or so much Partiality and Self-love, as to fansy it can't be better bestow'd than in making his; will yet be so honest and humble, as to think that 'tis fit she should take his Assistance, as Steward at least. For the good Man aspires no further, he would only take the Trouble of her Affairs off her Hand; and the Sense of her Condescension and his great Obligations, will for ever secure him against acting like a Lord and Master.

THE Steps to Folly, as well as Sin, are gradual, and almost imperceptible, and when we are once on the Decline, we go down without taking Notice on't; were it not for this, one could not account for those strange unequal Marriages we too often see. For there was a Time, no doubt, when a Woman could not have bore the very Thought of what she has been afterwards betray'd into; it would have appear'd as shocking to her, as it always does to other People; and had a Man been so impolitick as to discover the least Intimation of such a Design, he had given her a sufficient Antidote against it. This your wise Men are well satisfied of, and understand their own Interest too well to let their Design go bare-fac'd, for that would effectually put a Bar to their Success. So innocent are they, that they had not the least Thought at first of what their good Fortune afterwards leads them to! They would draw upon him, (if they wear a Sword) or fly in her Face who should let fall the least Hint that they had such Intentions; and this very Eagerness to avoid the Suspicion, is a shrewd Sign that there is Occasion for't.

But who shall dare to shew the Lady her Danger, when will it be seasonable to give her friendly Notice? If you do it ere she is resolv'd, though with all the Friendship and Tenderness imaginable, she will hardly forgive the Affront, or bear the Provocation; you offer her an Outrage by entertaining such a Thought, and 'tis ten to one if you are not afterwards accus'd for putting in her Head what otherwise she could ne'er have dreamt of. And when no direct Proof can be offer'd, when matter of Prudence is the only Thing in Question, every Body has so good an Opinion of their own Understanding, as to think their own Way the best. And when she has her Innocence and fair Intentions to oppose to your

Fears and Surmises, and you cannot pretend to wish her better than she does her self, to be more disinterested and diligent in your Watchfulness, or to see farther in what so nearly concerns her, what can be done? Her Ruin is commonly too far advanc'd to be prevented, ere you can in Good-breeding reach out a Hand to help her. For if the Train has took, if she is intangled in the Snare, if Love, or rather a blind unreasonable Fondness, which usurps the Name of that noble Passion, has gain'd on her, Reason and Persuasion may as properly be urg'd to the Folks in *Bethlem*, as to her. Tell her of this World, she is got above it, and has no Regard to its impertinent Censures; tell her of the next, she laughs at you, and will never be convinc'd that Actions which are not expressly forbid can be Criminal, though they proceed from, and must necessarily be reduc'd to ill Principles, though they give Offence, are of ill Example, injure our Reputation, which, next to our Innocence, we are obliged, as Christians, to take the greatest Care of; and, in a Word, do more Mischief than we can readily imagine. Tell her of her own Good, you appear yet more ridiculous, for who can judge of her Happiness but her self? And whilst our Hearts are violently set upon any thing, there is no convincing us that we shall ever be of another Mind. Our Passions want no Advocates, they are always furnish'd with plausible Pretences, and those very Prejudices, which gave rise to this unreasonable Passion, will for certain give her Obstinacy enough to justify and continue in it. Besides, some are so ill advis'd as to think to support one Indiscretion with another; they would not have it thought they had made a false Step, in once giving Countenance to that which is not fit to be continued. Or perhaps the Lady might be willing enough to throw off the Intruder at first, but wanted Courage to get above the Fear of his Calumnies, and the longer she suffers him to buz about her, she will find it the harder to get rid of his Importunities. By all which it appears, that she who really intends to be secure, must keep at the greatest Distance from Danger, she must not grant the *least* Indulgence, where such ill Uses will be made of it.

And since the Case is so, That Woman can never be in Safety who allows a Man Opportunity to betray her. Frequent Conversation does for certain produce either Aversion or Liking, and when 'tis once come to Liking, it depends on the Man's Generosity not to improve it farther, and where can one find an Instance that this is any Security? There are very many indeed which shew it is none. How sensible soever a Woman may appear of another's Indiscretion, if she will tread in the same Steps, though but for a little Way, she gives us no Assurance that she will not fall into the same Folly; she may perhaps intend very well, but she puts it past her Power to fulfil her good Intentions. Even those who have forfeited their Discretion, the most valuable Jewel next to their Vertue, and without which Vertue it self is but very weak and faint, 'tis like, were once as well resolv'd as she; they had the very same Thoughts, they made the same Apologies, and their Resentment would have been every whit as great against those who could have imagined they should so far forget themselves.

It were endless to reckon up the divers Stratagems Men use to catch their Prey, their different Ways of insinuating, which vary with Circumstances, and the Lady's Temper, but how unfairly, how basely soever they proceed, when the Prey is once caught, it passes for lawful Prize, and other Men having the same Hopes and Projects, see nothing to find Fault with, but that it was not their own good Fortune. They may exclaim against it perhaps in a Lady's Hearing, but it is only to keep themselves from being suspected, and to give the better Colour to their own Designs. Sometimes a Woman is cajol'd, and sometimes hector'd, she is seduc'd to love a Man, or aw'd into a Fear of him: He defends her Honour against another, or assumes the Power of blasting it himself; was willing to pass for one of no Consequence till he could make himself considerable at her Cost. He might be admitted at first to be *her Jest*, but he carries on the Humour so far till he makes her *his*; he will either entertain or serve her as Occasion offers, and some Way or other gets himself intrusted with her Fortune, her Fame, or her Soul. Allow him but a frequent and free Conversation, and there's no manner of Question but that his Ingenuity and Application, will, at one Time or other, get the Ascendant over her.

AND generally the more humble and undesigning a Man appears, the more improbable it looks that he should dare to pretend, the greater Caution should be us'd against him. A bold Address and good Assurance may sometimes, but does not always, take. To a Woman of Sense an artificial Modesty and Humility is a thousand times more dangerous, for he only draws back to receive the more Encouragement, and she regards not what Advances she makes towards him, who seems to understand himself and the World so well as to be incapable of making an ill Use of them. Would it not be unreasonable, and a Piece of Ill-breeding, to be shy of him who has no Pretensions, or only such as are Just and Modest? What Hurt in a Visit? Or what if Visits grow a little more frequent? The Man has so much Discernment, as to relish her Wit and Humour, and can she do less than be Partial to him who is so Just to her? He strives to please and to render himself agreeable, or necessary, perhaps, and whoever will make it his

Business, may find Ways enough to do it. For they know but little of Human Nature, they never consulted their own Hearts, who are not sensible what Advances a well-manag'd Flattery makes, especially from a Person of whose Wit and Sense one has a good Opinion. His Wit at first recommends his Flatteries, and these, in Requital, set off his Wit; and she who has been us'd to this high-season'd Diet, will scarce ever relish another Conversation.

HAVING got thus far, to be sure he is not wanting to his good Fortune, but drives on to an Intimacy, or what they are pleas'd, now a-days, though very unjustly, to call a Friendship; all is safe under this sacred Character, which sets them above little Aims and mean Designs. A Character that must be conducted with the nicest Honour, allows the greatest Trusts, leads to the highest Improvements, is attended with the purest Pleasures and most rational Satisfaction. And what if the malicious World, envious of his Happiness, should take Offence at it, since he has taken all due Precautions, such unjust and ill-natur'd Censures are not to be regarded; for his Part the Distance that is between them checks all aspiring Desires, but her Conversation is what he must not, cannot want: Life is insipid, and not to be endur'd without it; and he is too much the Lady's Friend, has too just a Value for her, to entertain a Thought to her Disadvantage.

Now if once it is come to this, GOD help the poor Woman! for not much Service can be done her by any of her Friends on Earth. That Pretender, to be sure, will be the Darling, he will worm out every other Person, though ever so kind and disinterested. For tho' true Friends will endeavour to please in order to serve, their Complaisance never goes so far as to prove injurious; the beloved Fault is what they chiefly strike at, and this the Flatterer always sooths; so that at last he becomes the most acceptable Company, and they who are conscious of their own Integrity, are not apt to bear such an unjust Distinction, nor is it by this Time to any Purpose to remonstrate the Danger of such an Intimacy. When a Man, and for certain much more when a Woman, is fallen into this Toil, that is, when either have been so unwary and indiscreet as to let another find out by what Artifices he may manage their Self-love, and draw it over to his Party, 'tis too late for any one who is really their Friend, to break the Snare and disabuse them.

NEITHER Sex cares to deny themselves that which pleases, especially when they think they may innocently indulge it; and nothing pleases more than the being Admir'd and Humour'd. We may be told of the Danger, and shewn the Fall of others, but though their Misfortunes are ever so often or so lively represented to us, we are all so well assur'd of our own good Conduct, as to believe it will bring us safe off those Rocks on which others have been Shipwreck'd. We suppose it in our Power to shorten the Line of our Liberty whenever we think fit, not considering that the farther we run, we shall be the more unwilling to retreat, and unable to judge when a Retreat is necessary. A Woman does not know that she is more than half lost when she admits of these Suggestions; that those Arguments she brings for continuing a Man's Conversation, prove only that she ought to have quitted it sooner; that Liking insensibly converts to Love, and that when she admits a Man to be her Friend, 'tis his Fault if he does not make himself her Husband.

AND if Men, even the Modestest and the Best, are only in pursuit of their own Designs, when they pretend to do the Lady Service; if the Honour they would seem to do her, tends only to lead her into an imprudent, and therefore a dishonourable Action; and they have all that good Opinion of themselves as to take every thing for Encouragement, so that she who goes beyond a bare Civility, though she meant no more than Respect, will find it interpreted a Favour, and made ill Use of, (for Favours, how innocent soever, never turn to a Lady's Advantage) what Shadow of a Pretence can a Woman have for admitting an Intimacy with a Man, whose Principles are known to be Loose, and his Practices Licentious?

can she expect to be safe with him who has ruin'd others, and by the very same Methods he takes with her? If an Intimacy with a Man of a fair Character gives Offence, with a Man of an ill one, 'tis doubly and trebly scandalous. And suppose neither her Fortune nor Beauty can tempt him, he has his ill-natur'd Pleasure in destroying that Vertue he will not practise, or if that can't be done, in blasting the Reputation of it at least, and in making the World believe he has made a Conquest, though he has found a Foil.

I꜠ the Man be the Woman's Inferior, besides all the Dangers formerly mention'd, and those just now taken Notice of, she gives such a Countenance to his Vices, as renders her in great measure, Partaker in them; and, it can scarce be thought in such Circumstances, a Woman could like the Man if she were not reconcil'd to his Faults. Is he her Equal, and no unsuitable Match, if his Designs are fair, why don't they Marry, since they are so well pleas'd with each other's Conversation, which in this State only can be frequently and safely allow'd? Is he her Better, and she hopes, by catching him, to make her Fortune, alas! the poor Woman is neither acquainted with the World nor her self; she neither knows her own Weakness, nor his Treachery, and though he gives her ever so much Encouragement to this vain Hope, 'tis only in order to accomplish her Ruin. To be sure the more Freedom she allows, the more she lessens his Esteem, and that's not likely to increase a real, though it may a pretended Kindness; she ought to fly, if she would have him pursue, the strictest Vertue and Reserve being the only Way to secure him.

RELIGION and Reputation are so sure a Guard, such a Security to poor defenceless Woman, that whenever a Man has ill Designs on her, he is sure to make a Breach into one or both of these, by endeavouring either to corrupt her Principles, to make her less strict in Devotion, or to lessen her Value of a fair Reputation, and would persuade her, that less than she imagines will secure her as to the next World, and that not much Regard is to be given to the Censures of this. Or if this be too bold at first, and will not pass with her, he has another Way to make even her Love to Vertue contribute to its Ruin, by persuading her it never shines as it ought, unless it is expos'd, and that she has no Reason to boast of her Vertue unless she has try'd it. An Opinion of the worst Consequence that may be, and the most mischievous to a Woman, because it is calculated to feed her Vanity, and tends indeed to her utter Ruin. For, can it be fit to rush into Temptations, when we are taught every Day to pray against them? If the Trials of our Vertue render it illustrious, 'tis such Trials as Heaven is pleas'd to send us, not those of our own seeking. It holds true of both Sexes, that next to the Divine Grace a modest Distrust of themselves is their best Security, none being so often and so shamefully foil'd, as those who depend most on their own Strength and Resolution.

As to the Opinion of the World, tho' one cannot say 'tis always just, yet generally it has a Foundation, great Regard is to be paid to it, and very good Use to be made of it. Others *may* be in Fault for passing their Censures, but we certainly *are* so, if we give them any the least just Occasion. And since Reputation is not only one of the Rewards of Vertue, that which always ought, and generally does attend it, but also a Guard against Evil, an Inducement to Good, and a great Instrument in the Hand of the Wise to promote the common Cause of Vertue; the being Prodigal of the one, looks as if we set no great Value on the other, and she who abandons her good Name, is not like to preserve her Innocence.

A Woman therefore can never have too nice a Sense of Honour, provided she does not prefer it before her Duty; she can never be too careful to secure her Character, not only from the Suspicion of a Crime, but even from the Shadow of an Indiscretion. 'Tis well worth her while to renounce the most Entertaining, and, what some perhaps, will call the most Improving Company, rather than give the World a just Occasion of Suspicion or Censure. For besides the Injury that is done Religion, which enjoins us to avoid the very Appearance of Evil, and to do nothing but what is of good Report, she puts her self too much in a Man's Power, who will run such a Risque for his Conversation, and expresses such a Value for him, as cannot fail of being made use of to do her a Mischief.

PRESERVE your Distance then, keep out of the Reach of Danger, fly if you would be safe, be sure to be always on the Reserve, not such as is Morose and Affected, but Modest and Discreet, your Caution cannot be too great, nor your Foresight reach too far; there's nothing, or what is next to nothing, a little Amusement and entertaining Conversation, lost by this, but all is hazarded by the other. A man understands his own Merit too well to lose his Time in a Woman's Company, were it not to divert himself at her Cost, to turn her into a Jest, or something worse. And where-ever you see great Assiduities, when a Man insinuates into the Diversions and Humours of the Lady, liking and admiring whatever she does, though at the same Time he seems to keep a due Distance, or rather exceeds in the profoundest Respect; Respect being all he dare at present pretend to: when a more than ordinary Deference is paid; when something particular appears in the Look and Address, and such an Obsequiousness in every Action, as nothing could engage a Man to, who never forgets the Superiority of his Sex, but a Hope to be observ'd in his Turn: Then, whatever the Inequality be, and how sensible soever he seems to be of it, the Man has for certain his Engines at work, the Mine is ready to be sprung on the first Opportunity, and 'tis well if it be not too late to prevent the poor Lady's Ruin.

To wind up this Matter; If a Woman were duly principled, and taught to know the World, especially the true Sentiments that Men have of her, and the Traps they lay for her under so many gilded Compliments, and such a seemingly great Respect, that Disgrace would be prevented which is brought upon too many Families; Women would Marry more discreetly, and demean themselves better in a married State, than some People say they do. The Foundation, indeed, ought to be laid deep and strong, she should be made a good Christian, and understand why she is so, and then she will be every thing else that is Good. Men need keep no Spies on a Woman's Conduct, need have no Fear of her Vertue, or so much as of her Prudence and Caution, were but a due Sense of true Honour and Vertue awaken'd in her; were her Reason excited and prepared to consider the Sophistry of those Temptations which would persuade her from her Duty; and were she put in a way to know that it is both her Wisdom and Interest to observe it: she would then duly examine and weigh all the Circumstances, the Good and Evil of a married State, and not be surprized with unforeseen Inconveniencies, and either never consent to be a Wife, or make a good one when she does. This would shew her what Human Nature *is*, as well as what it *ought* to be, and teach her not only what she may justly expect, but what she must be content with; would enable her to cure some Faults, and patiently to suffer what she cannot cure.

INDEED nothing can assure Obedience, and render it what it ought to be, but the Conscience of Duty, the paying it for GOD's sake. Superiors don't rightly understand their own Interest when they attempt to put out their Subjects Eyes to keep them Obedient. A blind Obedience is what a Rational Creature should never pay, nor would such an one receive it, did he rightly understand its Nature. For Human Actions are no otherwise valuable, than as they are conformable to Reason; but a blind Obedience is an Obeying *without Reason*, for ought we know, *against it*. GOD himself does not require our Obedience at this rate; he lays before us the Goodness and Reasonableness of his Laws, and were there any thing in them whose Equity we could not readily comprehend, yet we have this clear and sufficient Reason, on which, to found our Obedience, that nothing but what's just and fit, can be enjoin'd by a Just, a Wise, and Gracious GOD; but this is a Reason will never hold in respect of Mens Commands, unless they can prove themselves Infallible, and consequently Impeccable too.

It is therefore very much a Man's Interest, that Women should be good Christians; for in this, as in every other Instance, he who does his Duty, finds his own Account in it. Duty and true Interest are one and the same Thing, and he who thinks otherwise is to be pitied for being so much in the Wrong: But what can be more the Duty of the Head, than to instruct and improve those who are under Government? She will freely leave him the quiet Dominion of this World, whose Thoughts and Expectations are plac'd on the next. A Prospect of Heaven, and that only, will cure that Ambition which all generous Minds are fill'd with, not by taking it away, but by placing it on a right Object. She will discern a Time when her Sex shall be no Bar to the best Employments, the highest Honour; a Time when that Distinction, now so much us'd to her Prejudice, shall be no more; but, provided she is not wanting to her self, her Soul shall shine as bright as the greatest Heroe's. This is a true, and indeed, the only Consolation; this makes her a sufficient Compensation for all the Neglect and Contempt the ill-grounded Customs of the World throw on her; for all the Injuries brutal Power may do her, and is a sufficient Cordial to support her Spirits, be her Lot in this World what it may.

But some sage Persons may, perhaps object, that were Women allow'd to improve themselves, and not, amongst other Discouragements, driven back by the wise Jests and Scoffs that are put upon a Woman of Sense or Learning, a Philosophical Lady, as she is call'd by way of Ridicule; they would be too wise, and too good for the Men: I grant it, for vicious and foolish Men. Nor is it to be wonder'd that He is afraid he should not be able to Govern them were their Understandings improv'd, who is resolv'd not to take too much Pains with his own. But these, 'tis to be hoped, are no very considerable Number, the Foolish at least; and therefore this is so far from being an Argument against Womens Improvement, that it is a strong one for it, if we do but suppose the Men to be as capable of Improvement as the Women; but much more, if, according to Tradition, we believe they have greater Capacities. This, if any thing, would stir them up to be what they ought, and not permit them to waste their Time and abuse their Faculties in the Service of their irregular Appetites and unreasonable Desires, and so let poor contemptible Women, who have been their Slaves, excel them in all that is truly excellent. This would make them Blush at employing an immortal Mind no better than in making Provision for the Flesh to fulfil the Lusts thereof, since Women, by a wiser Conduct, have brought themselves to such a Reach of Thought, to such Exactness of Judgment, such Clearness and Strength of Reasoning, such Purity and Elevation of

Mind, such Command of their Passions, such Regularity of Will and Affection, and, in a Word, to such a Pitch of Perfection, as the Human Soul is capable of attaining in this Life by the Grace of GOD; such true Wisdom, such real Greatness, as though it does not qualify them to make a Noise in this World, to found or overturn Empires, yet it qualifies them for what is infinitely better, a Kingdom that cannot be mov'd, an incorruptible Crown of Glory.

BESIDES, it were ridiculous to suppose, that a Woman, were she ever so much improv'd, could come near the topping Genius of the Men, and therefore why should they envy or discourage her? Strength of Mind goes along with Strength of Body, and 'tis only for some odd Accidents which Philosophers have not yet thought worth while to enquire into, that the sturdiest Porter is not the wisest Man! As therefore the Men have the Power in their Hands, so there's no Dispute of their having the Brains to manage it! Can we suppose there is such a Thing as good Judgment and Sense upon Earth, if it is not to be found among them: Do not they, generally speaking, do all the great Actions and considerable Business of this World, and leave that of the next to the Women? Their Subtlety in forming Cabals and laying deep Designs, their Courage and Conduct in breaking through all Tyes, sacred and civil, to effect them, not only advances them to the Post of Honour, and keeps them securely in it for twenty or thirty Years, but gets them a Name, and conveys it down to Posterity for some Hundreds; and who would look any further? Justice and Injustice are administred by their Hands, Courts and Schools are fill'd with these Sages; 'tis Men who dispute for Truth, as well as Men who argue against it: Histories are writ by them; they recount each other's great Exploits, and have always done so. All famous Arts have their Original from Men, even from the Invention of Guns, to the Mystery of good Eating. And to shew that nothing is beneath their Care, any more than above their Reach, they have brought *Gaming* to an Art and Science, and a more Profitable and Honourable one too, than any of those that us'd to be call'd *Liberal*! Indeed, what is it they can't perform, when they attempt it? The Strength of their Brains shall be every whit as conspicuous at their Cups, as in a Senate-House, and, when they please, they can make it pass for as sure a Mark of Wisdom, to drink deep, as to reason profoundly; a greater Proof of Courage, and consequently of Understanding, to dare the Vengeance of Heaven it self, than to stand the Raillery of some of the worst of their Fellow Creatures!

AGAIN, it may be said, If a Wife's Case be as it is here represented, it is not good for a Woman to marry, and so there's an End of Human Race. But this is no fair Consequence, for all that can justly be inferr'd from hence, is, that a Woman has no mighty Obligations to the Man who makes Love to her; she has no Reason to be fond of being a Wife, or to reckon it a Piece of Preferment when she is taken to be a Man's Upper-Servant; it is no Advantage to her in this World; if rightly manag'd it may prove one as to the next. For she who marries purely to do good, to educate Souls for Heaven, who can be so truly mortified as to lay aside her own Will and Desires, to pay such an intire Submission for Life, to one whom she cannot be sure will always deserve it, does certainly perform a more Heroick Action, than all the famous Masculine Heroes can boast of, she suffers a continual Martyrdom to bring Glory to GOD, and Benefit to Mankind; which Consideration, indeed, may carry her through all Difficulties, I know not what else can, and engage her to Love him who proves perhaps so much worse than a Brute, as to make this Condition yet more grievous than it needed to be. She has need of a strong Reason, of a truly Christian and well-temper'd Spirit, of all the Assistance the best Education can give her, and ought to have some good Assurance of her own Firmness and Vertue, who ventures on such a Trial; and for this Reason 'tis less to be wonder'd at that Women marry off in haste, for perhaps if they took Time to consider and reflect upon it, they seldom would marry.

To conclude. Perhaps I've said more than most Men will thank me for; I cannot help it, for how much soever I may be their Friend and humble Servant, I am more a Friend to Truth. Truth is strong, and some time or other will prevail; nor is it for their Honour, and therefore one would think not for their Interest, to be partial to themselves and unjust to others. They may fancy I have made some Discoveries, which, like *Arcana Imperii*, ought to be kept secret; but, in good earnest, I do them more Honour than to suppose their lawful Prerogatives need any mean Arts to support them. If they have usurp'd, I love Justice too much to wish Success and Continuance to Usurpations, which, though submitted to out of Prudence, and for Quietness sake, yet leave everybody free to regain their lawful Right whenever they have Power and Opportunity. I don't say that Tyranny *ought*, but we find in *Fact*, that it provokes the Oppress'd to throw off even a lawful Yoke that fits too heavy: And if he who is freely elected, after all his fair Promises, and the fine Hopes he rais'd, proves a Tyrant, the Consideration that he was one's own Choice, will not render one more Submissive and Patient, but I fear, more Refractory. For though it is very unreasonable, yet we see 'tis the Course of the World, not only to return Injury for Injury, but Crime for Crime; both Parties indeed are Guilty, but the Aggressors have a double Guilt, they have not only their own, but their Neighbour's Ruin to answer for.

As to the Female Reader, I hope she will allow I've endeavoured to do her Justice; not betray'd her Cause as her Advocates usually do, under Pretence of defending it. A Practice too mean for any to be guilty of who have the least Sense of Honour, and who do any more than meerly pretend to it. I think I have held the Balance even, and not being conscious of Partiality, I ask no Pardon for it. To plead for the Oppress'd, and to defend the Weak, seem'd to me a generous Undertaking; for though it may be secure, 'tis not always Honourable, to run over to the strongest Party. And if she infers from what has been said, that Marriage is a very happy State for Men, if they think fit to make it so; that they govern the World, they have Prescription on their Side; Women are too weak to dispute it with them, therefore they, as all other Governors, are most, if not only, accountable for what's amiss; for whether other Governments in their Original, were or were not confer'd according to the Merit of the Person, yet certainly in this Case, if Heaven has appointed the Man to govern, it has Qualified him for it: So far I agree with her: But if she goes on to infer, that therefore, if a Man has not these Qualifications, where is his Right? That if he misemploys, he abuses it? And if he abuses, according to modern Deduction, he forfeits it, I must leave her there. A peaceable Woman, indeed, will not carry it so far, she will neither question her Husband's Right, nor his Fitness to govern, but how? Not as an absolute Lord and Master, with an arbitrary and tyrannical Sway, but as Reason governs and conducts a Man, by proposing what is just and fit. And the Man who acts according to that Wisdom he assumes, who would have that Superiority he pretends to, acknowledged just, will receive no Injury by any thing that has been offered here. A Woman will value Him the more who is so wise and good, when she discerns how much he excels the rest of his noble Sex; the less he requires, the more will he merit that Esteem and Deference, which those who are so forward to exact, seem conscious they don't deserve. So then the Man's Prerogative is not at all infring'd, whilst the Woman's Privileges are secured; and if any Woman think her self injur'd, she has a Remedy in reserve, which few Men will envy, or endeavour to rob her of, the Exercise and Improvement of her Vertue Here, and the Reward of it Hereafter.

WHEN I made these Reflections, I was of Opinion, that the Case of married Women, in comparison of that of their Husbands, was not a little hard and unequal. But as the World now goes, I am apt to think, that a Husband is in no desirable Situation; his

Honour is in his Wife's keeping, and what Man of Honour can be satisfied with the Conduct which the Licentiousness of the Age not only permits, but would endeavour to authorize as a Part of good Breeding? And what makes his Case the worse, he must dissemble his Uneasiness, stifle his Resentments, and not dare to take the proper Methods of preventing and curing the Disorder.

So great is our Corruption, that such as pretend to make a true Estimate of Human Life, and very freely Satirize both Sexes for lesser Crimes, are not asham'd to recommend this, prescribing a known Sin as a Cure for what is not absolutely unlawful in it self, though very pernicious in its Consequences, when carried to Excess.

NOT that I would in any manner apologize for Gaming, which, when carried to Excess, is ruinous to both Sexes, especially to Women; who, when given to this Vice, disregard their Husbands, and Oeconomy, neglect the Education of their Children, spend their Fortunes as much as they can, and, which is not the least Inconveniency, when they lose to Men more than they are able to pay, they give their Creditor Opportunity to make insolent Demands. But sure, any Husband, who is not sunk to the lowest Degree of Infamy, had rather his Wife should waste his Money at *Quadrille*, than Intrigue with a *Colonel*. *If Sin you must* (says an admirable Author, whose

Panegyricks are Satires, and his Satires Panegyricks) —*take Nature for your Guide, Love has some soft Excuse to sooth your Pride.*

CAN we read this excellent Advice of this very moral Satirist, without remembring what the *Psalmist* says of some of his Contemporaries; *When thou sawest a Thief thou consentedst unto him, and hast been Partaker with the Adulterer?* For, sure of all other Thieves he is the most criminal, who (under Pretence of Friendship, perhaps) robs a Man of his most valued Effects, deprives him of his Honour, and of the Quiet and Comfort of his Life.

NATURE and LOVE, as they, injuriously to both, miscall their brutal Appetite, are very different from what our Author would represent them. Variety by no Means answers the End of Nature in providing for Posterity. And enough has been said, to shew, that such Professions of Love are most abusive, and the Effect of their Passion the most outrageous Injury that Hatred can produce: A Woman is never so effectually *humbled*, as the Scripture elegantly expresses it, as when a Man obtains his Desires. And if she consents, she renders her self despicable in his Eyes as well as in the Eyes of others. Thus the *English* Muse very truly sings:

*That wretched She, who yields to guilty Joys,*
*A man may Pity, but he MUST Despise.*

93

WHOEVER makes a true Estimate of Christianity, who does not profess it, because as yet, 'tis the Religion of his Country, or for his Interest, or some such worthy Motive; but upon full Conviction of its Divine Authority, which he cannot want if he examines impartially, as a Matter of this Consequence deserves; such a Man will find Christianity requires the strictest Purity of Heart and Imagination, since in the thickest Darkness our Thoughts, as well as our Actions, are manifest to our Judge; and, that whoever looks upon a Woman to Lust after her, has committed Adultery with her already in his Heart.

*Horses and Bulls, and all the brutal Kind,*
*Range o'er the Field, to no one She confin'd,*
*They know not Love, for Love is in the Mind.*
*These following Nature are exempt from Blame,*
*Unconscious or of Guilt, Remorse and Shame.*

*But Man, unhappy Man! puts out his Light,*
*Reason forsakes, to follow Appetite.*
*Sinks down to Brute, and labours but in vain,*
*To be like them, without Remorse or Shame;*
*To Guilt, inevitably follows Pain.*

*No Deeds of Darkness are conceal'd by Night,*
*He sees Who dwells in everlasting Light,*
*And ev'ry Thought is open to His Sight.*

# *APPENDIX*

THE *Reflector*, who hopes *Reflector* is not bad *English*, (now *Governor* is happily of the Feminine Gender) guarded against Curiosity in vain: For a certain ingenuous Gentleman, as she is inform'd, had the Good-nature to own these Reflections, so far, as to affirm that he had the Original *MS.* in his Closet, a Proof she is not able to produce; and so to make himself responsible for all their Faults, for which, she returns him all due Acknowledgement. However, the Generality being of Opinion, that a Man would have had more Prudence and Manners than to have Publish'd such unseasonable Truths, or to have betray'd the *Arcana Imperii* of his Sex; she humbly confesses, that the Contrivance and Execution of this Design, which is unfortunately accus'd of being so destructive to the Government, (of the Men, I mean) is intirely her own. She neither advis'd with Friends, nor turn'd over antient or modern Authors, nor prudently submitted to the Correction of such as are, or such as *think* they are good Judges, but with an *English* spirit and Genius, set out upon the Forlorn Hope, meaning no Hurt to any body, nor designing any thing but the publick Good, and to retrieve, if possible, the

Native Liberty, the Rights and Privileges of the Subject.

FAR be it from her to stir up Sedition of any sort: none can abhor it more; and she heartily wishes, that our Masters would pay their Civil and Ecclesiastical Governors the same Submission, which they themselves exact from their Domestick Subjects. Nor can she imagine how she any way undermines the Masculine Empire, or blows the Trumpet of Rebellion to the Moiety of Mankind. Is it by exhorting Women, not to expect to have their own Will in any thing, but to be intirely Submissive, when once they have made Choice of a Lord and Master, though he happen not to be so wise, so kind, or even so just a Governor as was expected? She did not, indeed, advise them to think his Folly Wisdom, nor his Brutality, that Love and Worship he promised in his Matrimonial Oath; for this required a Flight of Wit and Sense much above her poor Ability, and proper only to Masculine Understandings. However, she did not in any manner prompt them to Resist, or to Abdicate the Perjur'd Spouse, though the Laws of GOD, and the Land, make special Provision for it, in a Case, wherein, as is to be fear'd, few Men can truly plead Not Guilty.

'TIS true, through want of Learning, and of that

Superior Genius which Men, as Men, lay claim to, she was ignorant of the *Natural Inferiority* of our Sex, which our Masters lay down as a Self-evident and Fundamental Truth. She saw nothing in the Reason of Things, to make this either a Principle or a Conclusion, but much to the contrary; it being Sedition at least, if not Treason, to assert it in this Reign. For if by the Natural Superiority of their Sex, they mean, that *every* Man is by Nature superior to *every* Woman, which is the obvious Meaning, and that which must be stuck to if they would speak Sense, it would be a Sin in *any* Woman, to have Dominion over *any* Man, and the greatest Queen ought not to command, but to obey, her Footman: because no Municipal Laws can supersede or change the Law of Nature: So that if the Dominion of the Men be such, the *Salique Law*, as unjust as *English Men* have ever thought it, ought to take Place over all the Earth, and the most glorious Reigns in the *English, Danish, Castilian*, and other Annals, were wicked Violations of the Law of Nature!

If they mean that *some* Men are superior to *some* Women, this is no great Discovery; had they turn'd the Tables, they might have seen that *some* Women are superior to *some* Men. Or had they been pleased to remember their Oaths of Allegiance and Supremacy, they might have known, that *One* Woman is superior to *All* the Men in these Nations, or else they have sworn to very little Purpose. And it must not be suppos'd, that their Reason and Religion would suffer them to take Oaths, contrary to the Law of Nature and Reason of Things.

By all which it appears, that our Reflector's Ignorance is very pitiable; it may be her Misfortune, but not her Crime, especially since she is willing to be better inform'd, and hopes she shall never be so obstinate as to shut her Eyes against the Light of Truth, which is not to be charg'd with Novelty, how late soever we may be bless'd with the Discovery. Nor can Error, be it as antient as it may, ever plead Prescription against Truth. And since the only way to remove all Doubts, to answer all Objections, and to give the Mind entire Satisfaction, is not by *Affirming*, but by *Proving*, so that every one may see with their *own* Eyes, and judge according to the best of their *own* Understandings; she hopes it is no Presumption to insist on this Natural Right of Judging for her self, and the rather, because by quitting it, we give up all the Means of Rational Conviction. Allow us then as many Glasses as you please to help our Sight, and as many good Arguments as you can afford to convince our Understandings: But don't exact of us, we beseech you, to affirm that we see such Things as are only the Discovery of Men who have quicker Senses; or, that we understand, and know what we have by Hear-say only; for to be so excessively Complaisant, is neither to see nor to understand.

THAT the Custom of the World, has put Women, generally speaking, into a State of Subjection, is not denied; but the Right can no more be prov'd from the Fact, than the Predominancy of Vice can justify it. A certain great Man, has endeavour'd to prove, by Reasons not contemptible, that in the Original State of Things the Woman was the Superior, and that her Subjection to the Man is an Effect of the Fall, and the Punishment of her Sin: And, that ingenious Theorist Mr. *Whiston*, asserts, That before the Fall there was a greater Equality between the two Sexes. However this be, 'tis certainly no Arrogance in a Woman to conclude, that she was made for the Service of GOD, and that this is her End. Because GOD made all Things for Himself, and a rational Mind is too noble a Being to be made for the Sake and Service of any Creature. The Service she at any Time becomes oblig'd to pay to a Man, is only a Business by the Bye, just as it may be any Man's Business and Duty to keep Hogs; he was not Made for this, but if he Hires himself out to such an Employment, he ought conscientiously to perform it. Nor can any thing be concluded to the contrary from St. *Paul's* Argument, I *Cor.* xi. for he argues only for Decency and Order, according to the present Custom and State of Things: Taking his Words strictly and literally, they prove too much, in that, *Praying and Prophecying in the Church* are allow'd the Women, provided they do it with their Head cover'd as well as the Men, and no Inequality can be inferr'd from hence, neither from the Gradation the Apostle there uses, that *the Head of every Man is Christ, and that the Head of the Woman is the Man, and the Head of Christ is* GOD; it being evident from the Form of Baptism, that there is no natural Inferiority among the Divine Persons, but that they are in all Things Coequal. The Apostle, indeed, adds, that *the Man is the Glory of* GOD, *and the Woman the Glory of Man,* &c. But what does he infer from hence? He says not a Word of Inequality, or natural Inferiority; but concludes, that a Woman ought to cover her Head, and a Man ought not to cover his, and *that even Nature it self teaches* us, that *if a Man have long Hair it is a Shame unto him.* Whatever the Apostle's Argument proves in this Place, nothing can be plainer, than that there is much more said against the present Fashion of Mens wearing long Hair, than for that Supremacy they lay claim to. For by all that appears in the Text, it is not so much a Law of Nature, that Women should obey Men, as that Men should not wear long Hair. Now how can a Christian Nation allow Fashions contrary to the Law of Nature, forbidden by an Apostle, and declared by him to be a Shame to Men? Or if Custom may make an Alteration in one Case, it may in another, but what then becomes of the Nature and Reason of Things? Besides, the Conclusion the Apostle draws from his Argument concerning Women, *viz.* that they *should have Power on their Heads because of the Angels*, is so very obscure a Text, that that ingenious Paraphrast, who pleads so much for the *Natural Subjection* of Women, ingeniously confesses, that he does not understand it. Probably it refers to some Custom among the *Corinthians*, which being well known to them, the Apostle only hints at it, but which we are ignorant of, and therefore apt to mistake him. 'Tis like, that the false Apostle whom St. *Paul* writes against, had *led Captive* some of their rich and powerful, but *silly Women*, who having as mean an Opinion of the Reason GOD had given them, as any Deceiver could desire, did not, like the noble-minded *Bereans*, *search the Scriptures whether those*

*Things were so*, but lazily took up with having Mens Persons in admiration, and follow'd their Leaders blindfold, the certain Rout to Destruction. And it is also probable, that the same cunning Seducer imploy'd these Women to carry on his own Designs, and putting them upon what he might not think fit to appear in himself, made them guilty of indecent Behaviour in the Church of *Corinth*. And therefore St. *Paul* thought it necessary to reprove them so severely, in order to humble them; but this being done, he takes care in the Conclusion to set the Matter on a right Foot, placing the two Sexes on a Level, to keep Men, as much as might be, from taking those Advantages which People who have Strength in their Hands, are apt to assume over those who can't contend with them. For, says he, *Nevertheless*, or notwithstanding the former Argument, *the Man is not without the Woman, nor the Woman without the Man, but all Things of* GOD. The Relation between the two Sexes is mutual, and the Dependence reciprocal, both of them depending intirely upon GOD, and upon Him only; which, one would think, is no great Argument of the natural Inferiority of either Sex.

OUR *Reflector* is of Opinion, that Disputes of this kind, extending to Human Nature in general, and not peculiar to those to whom the Word of GOD has been reveal'd, ought to be decided by Natural Reason only. And, that the Holy Scripture should not be interested in the present Controversy, in which it determines nothing, any more than it does between the *Copernican* and *Ptolomean* Systems. The Design of those Holy Books being to make us excellent Moralists and perfect Christians, not great Philosophers; and being writ for the Vulgar as well as for the Learned, they are accommodated to the common way of Speech and the Usage of the World; in which we have but a short Probation, so that it matters not much what Part we act, whether of Governing or Obeying, provided we perform it well with respect to the World to come.

ONE does not wonder, indeed, that when an Adversary is drove to a Non-plus, and Reason declares against him, he flies to Authority, especially to Divine, which is infallible, and therefore ought not to be disputed. But Scripture is not always on their Side who make Parade of it, and through their Skill in Languages, and the Tricks of the Schools, wrest it from its genuine Sense to their own Inventions. And supposing, not granting, that it were apparently to the Womens Disadvantage, no fair and generous Adversary but would be asham'd to urge this Advantage: Because Women, without their own Fault, are kept in Ignorance of the Original, wanting Languages and other Helps to Criticise on the Sacred Text, of which, they know no more, than Men are pleas'd to impart in their Translations. In short, they shew their Desire to maintain their Hypotheses, but by no means their Reverence to the Sacred Oracles, who engage them in such Disputes. And therefore, the Blame be theirs, who have unnecessarily introduc'd them in the present Subject, and who, by saying, that the *Reflections* were not agreeable to Scripture, oblige the Reflector to shew, that those who affirm it must either mistake her Meaning, or the Sense of Holy Scripture, or both, if they think what they say, and do not find fault meerly because they resolve to do so. For, had she ever writ any thing contrary to those sacred Truths, she would be the first in pronouncing its Condemnation.

BUT what says the Holy Scripture? It speaks of Women as in a State of Subjection, and so it does of the *Jews* and *Christians*, when under the Dominion of the *Chaldeans* and *Romans*, requiring of the one as well as of the other, a quiet Submission to them under whose Power they liv'd. But will any one say, that these had a *Natural Superiority* and Right to Dominion? that they had a superior Understanding, or any Pre-eminence, except what their greater

Strength acquir'd? Or, that the other were subjected to their Adversaries for any other Reason but the Punishment of their Sins, and, in order to their Reformation? Or for the Exercise of their Vertue, and because the Order of the World and the Good of Society requir'd it?

If Mankind had never Sin'd, Reason would always have been obeyed, there would have been no Struggle for Dominion, and Brutal Power would not have prevail'd. But in the lapsed State of Mankind, and now, that Men will not be guided by their Reason but by their Appetites, and do not what they *ought* but what they *can*, the Reason, or that which stands for it, the Will and Pleasure of the Governor, is to be the Reason of those who will not be guided by their own, and must take Place for Order's sake, although it should not be conformable to right Reason. Nor can there be any Society great or little, from Empires down to private Families, without a last Resort, to determine the Affairs of that Society by an irresistible Sentence. Now unless this Supremacy be fix'd somewhere, there will be a perpetual Contention about it, such is the Love of Dominion, and let the Reason of Things be what it may, those who have least Force or Cunning to supply it, will have the Disadvantage. So that since Women are acknowledged to have least Bodily Strength, their being commanded to Obey is in pure Kindness to them, and for their Quiet and Security, as well as for the Exercise of their Vertue. But does it follow, that Domestick Governors have more Sense than their Subjects, any more than that other Governors have? We do not find that any Man thinks the worse of his own Understanding, because another has superior Power; or concludes himself less capable of a Post of Honour and Authority, because he is not prefer'd to it. How much Time would lie on Mens Hands, how empty would the Places of Concourse be, and how silent most Companies, did Men forbear to censure their Governors, that is, in effect, to think themselves wiser. Indeed, Government would be much more desirable than it is, did it invest the Possessor with a superior Understanding as well as Power. And if meer Power gives a Right to Rule, there can be no such Thing as Usurpation; but a Highway-Man, so long as he has Strength to force, has also a Right to require our Obedience.

AGAIN, if absolute Sovereignty be not necessary in a State, how comes it to be so in a Family? Or if in a Family why not in a State; since no Reason can be alledged for the one that will not hold more strongly for the other? If the Authority of the Husband, so far as it extends, is sacred and inalienable, why not that of the Prince? The Domestick Sovereign is without Dispute elected, and the Stipulations and Contract are mutual; is it not then partial in Men to the last Degree, to contend for, and practise that Arbitrary Dominion in their Families, which they abhor and exclaim against in the State? For if Arbitrary Power is evil in it self, and an improper Method of Governing Rational and Free Agents, it ought not to be practis'd any where; nor is it less, but rather more mischievous in Families than in Kingdoms, by how much 100,000 Tyrants are worse than one. What though a Husband can't deprive a Wife of Life without being responsible to the Law, he may, however, do what is much more grievous to a generous Mind, render Life miserable, for which she has no Redress, scarce Pity, which is afforded to every other Complainant, it being thought a Wife's Duty to suffer every thing without Complaint. If *all Men are born Free*, how is it that all Women are born Slaves? As they must be, if the being subjected to the *inconstant, uncertain, unknown, arbitrary Will* of Men, be the *perfect Condition of Slavery?* And, if the Essence of Freedom consists, as our Masters say it does, in having a *standing Rule to live by?* And why is Slavery so much condemn'd and strove against in one Case, and so highly applauded, and held so necessary and so sacred in another?

'Tis true, that God told *Eve* after the Fall, that *her Husband should Rule over her:* And so it is, that he told *Esau* by the Mouth of *Isaac* his Father, that he should *serve* his *younger Brother*, and should in Time, when he was strong enough to do it, *break the Yoke from off his Neck*. Now, why one Text should be a Command any more than the other, and not both of them be Predictions only; or why the former should prove *Adam's* Natural Right to Rule, and much less every Man's, any more than the latter is a Proof of *Jacob's* Right to Rule, and of *Esau's* to Rebel, one is yet to learn? The Text in both Cases foretelling what would be; but neither of them determining what *ought* to be.

But the Scripture commands *Wives* to *submit themselves to their own Husbands*. True; for which St. *Paul* gives a Mystical Reason (*Eph.* v. 22, *&c.*) and St. *Peter*, a Prudential and Charitable one (I *Pet.* iii.) but neither of them derive that Subjection from the Law of Nature. Nay, St. *Paul*, as if he foresaw and meant to prevent this Plea, giving Directions for their Conduct to Women in general, I *Tim.* ii. when he comes to speak of *Subjection*, he changes his Phrase from *Women*, which denotes the whole Sex, to *Woman*, which in the New Testament is appropriated to a Wife.

As for his not suffering Women to speak in the Church, no sober Person that I know of pretends to it. That learned Paraphrast, indeed, who lays so much Stress on the *Natural Subjection*, provided this Prerogative be secur'd, is willing to give up the other. For he endeavours to prove, that Inspir'd Women, as well as Men, us'd to speak in the Church, and that St. *Paul* does not forbid it, but only takes care that the Women should signify their Subjection by wearing a Veil. But the Apostle is his own best Expositor, let us therefore compare his Precepts with his Practice, for he was all of a Piece, and did not contradict himself. Now by this Comparison we find, that though he forbids Women to teach in the Church, and this for several Prudential Reasons, like those he introduces with an *I give my Opinion, and now speak I, not the Lord*, and not because of any Law of Nature, or positive Divine Precept, for that the Words *they are commanded* (I *Cor.* xiv. 24.) are not in the Original, appears from the *Italick* Character, yet he did not found this Prohibition on any suppos'd want of Understanding in Woman, or of Ability to teach; neither does he confine them at all Times to *learn in Silence*. For the eloquent *Apollos*, who was himself a Teacher, was instructed by *Priscilla*, as well as by her Husband *Aquila*, and was improv'd by them both in the Christian Faith. Nor does St. *Paul* blame her for this, or suppose that she *usurp'd Authority over* that great *Man;* so far from this, that as she is always honourably mention'd in Holy Scripture, so our Apostle, in his Salutations, *Rom.* xvi. places her in the Front, even before her Husband, giving to her, as well as to him, the Noble Title of, *his Helper in Christ Jesus*, and of one *to whom all the Churches of the* Gentiles had great Obligations.

BUT, it will be said perhaps, that in I *Tim.* ii. 13, *&c.* St. *Paul* argues for the Woman's Subjection from the Reason of Things. To this I answer, that it must be confess'd, that this (according to the vulgar Interpretation) is a very obscure Place, and I should be glad to see a Natural, and not a Forc'd Interpretation given of it by those who take it Literally: Whereas if it be taken Allegorically, with respect to the Mystical Union between Christ and his Church, to which St. *Paul* frequently accommodates the Matrimonial Relation, the Difficulties vanish. For the Earthly *Adam's* being *form'd* before *Eve*, seems as little to prove her Natural Subjection to him, as the living Creatures, Fishes, Birds and Beasts being form'd before them both, proves that Mankind must be subject to these Animals. Nor can the Apostle mean that *Eve* only sinned; or that she only was *Deceiv'd*, for if *Adam* sinn'd wilfully and knowingly, he became the greater Transgressor. But it is very true, that the Second *Adam*, the Man Christ Jesus, *was first form'd*, and then his Spouse the Church. He was not in any respect *Deceiv'd*, nor does she pretend to Infallibility. And from this second *Adam*, promis'd to *Eve* in the Day of our first Parents Transgression, and from Him only, do all their Race, Men as well as Women, derive their Hopes of Salvation. Nor is it promis'd to either Sex on any other Terms besides Perseverance in *Faith, Charity, Holiness and Sobriety*.

IF the Learned will not admit of this Interpretation, I know not how to contend with them. For Sense is a Portion that GOD Himself has been pleased to distribute to both Sexes with an impartial Hand, but Learning is what Men have engross'd to themselves, and one can't but admire their great Improvements! For, after doubting whether there is such a Thing as Truth, and after many hundred Years Disputes about it, in the last Century an extraordinary Genius arose, (whom yet, some are pleased to call a Visionary) enquir'd after it, and laid down the best Method of finding it. Not to the general Liking of the Men of Letters, perhaps, because it was wrote in a vulgar Language, and was so natural and easy as to debase Truth to common Understandings, shewing too plainly, that Learning and true Knowledge are two very different Things.

For it often happens (says that Author) that Women and Children acknowledge the Falsehood of those Prejudices we contend with, because they do not dare to judge without Examination, and they bring all the Attention they are capable of to what they read. Whereas on the contrary, the Learned continue wedded to their own Opinions, because they will not take the Trouble of examining what is contrary to their receiv'd Doctrines.

SCIENCES, indeed, have been invented and taught long ago, and, as Men grew better advis'd, new modelled. So that it is become a considerable Piece of Learning to give an Account of the Rise and Progress of the Sciences, and of the various Opinions of Men concerning them. But Certainty and Demonstration are much pretended to in this present Age, and being obtain'd in many Things, 'tis hoped Men will never Dispute them away in that which is of greatest Importance, the Way of Salvation. And because there is not any thing more certain than what is delivered in the Oracles of GOD, we come now to consider what they offer in Favour of our Sex.

LET it be promis'd, (according to the Reasoning of a very ingenious Person in a like Case) that one Text for us, is more to be regarded than many against us. Because that *One* being different from what Custom has established, ought to be taken with Philosophical Strictness; whereas the *Many* being express'd according to the vulgar Mode of Speech, ought to have no greater Stress laid on them, than that evident Condescension will bear. One Place then were sufficient, but we have many Instances wherein Holy Scripture considers Women very differently from what they appear in the common Prejudices of Mankind.

THE World will hardly allow a Woman to say any thing well, unless, as she borrows it from Men, or as assisted by them: But GOD Himself allows that the Daughters of *Zelophehad spake right,* and passes their Request into a Law. Considering how much the Tyranny, shall I say, or the superior Force of Men, keeps Women from Acting in the World, or doing any thing considerable, and remembring withal the Conciseness of the Sacred Story, no small Part of it is bestow'd in transmitting the History of Women, famous in their Generations: Two of the Canonical Books, bearing the Names of those great Women whose Vertues and Actions are there recorded. *Ruth* being call'd from among the *Gentiles* to be an Ancestor of the Messiah, and *Esther* being rais'd up by GOD to be the great Instrument of the Deliverance and Prosperity of the *Jewish* Church.

THE Character of *Isaac*, though one of the most blameless Men taken Notice of in the Old Testament, must give Place to *Rebecca's*, whose Affections are more reasonably plac'd than his, her Favourite Son being the same who was GOD's Favourite. Nor was the Blessing bestow'd according to his, but to her Desire; so that if you will not allow, that her Command to *Jacob* superseded *Isaac's* to *Esau*, his Desire to give the Blessing to this Son, being evidently an Effect of his Partiality; you must at least grant, that she paid greater Deference to the Divine Revelation, and for this Reason, at least, had a Right to oppose her Husband's Design; which, it seems, *Isaac* was sensible of, when upon his Disappointment, he *trembled so exceedingly*. And so much Notice is taken even of *Rebecca's* Nurse, that we have an Account where she died, and where she was buried.

GOD is pleas'd to Record it among His Favours to the ingrateful *Jews*, that He sent before them His Servants *Moses*, *Aaron*, and MIRIAM; who was also a Prophetess, and instructed the Women how to bear their Part with *Moses* in his Triumphal Hymn. Is she to be blam'd for her Ambition? And is not the

High Priest *Aaron* also, who has his Share in the Reproof as well as in the Crime? nor could she have mov'd Sedition if she had not been a considerable Person, which appears also by the Respect the People paid her, in deferring their Journey till she was ready.

WHERE shall we find a nobler Piece of Poetry than *Deborah*'s Song? Or a better and greater Ruler than that renowned Woman, whose Government so much excelled that of the former Judges? And though she had a Husband, she her self judged *Israel*, and consequently was his Sovereign, of whom we know no more than the Name. Which Instance, as I humbly suppose, overthrows the Pretence of *Natural Inferiority*. For it is not the bare Relation of a Fact, by which none ought to be concluded, unless it is conformable to a Rule, and to the Reason of Things: But *Deborah*'s Government was conferr'd on her by GOD Himself. Consequently the Sovereignty of a Woman is not contrary to the Law of Nature; for the Law of Nature is the Law of GOD, who cannot contradict Himself; and yet it was GOD who inspir'd and approv'd that great Woman, raising her up to Judge and to Deliver His People *Israel*.

NOT to insist on the Courage of that valiant Woman, who deliver'd *Thebez* by slaying the Assailant; nor upon the Preference which GOD thought fit to give to *Sampson*'s Mother, in sending the Angel to

her, and not to her Husband, whose vulgar Fear she
so prudently answer'd, as plainly shews her superior
Understanding; To pass over *Abigail's* wise Conduct,
whereby she preserv'd her Family and deserved
*David's* Acknowledgments, for restraining him from
doing a rash and unjustifiable Action; the Holy Pen-
man giving her the Character of a *Woman of good
Understanding*, whilst her Husband has that of a
Churlish and Foolish Person, and a Son of *Belial:* To
say nothing of the *wise Woman* (as the Text calls
her) of *Tekoah;* or of her of *Abel*, who has the same
Epithet, and who by her Prudence delivered the City
and appeas'd a dangerous Rebellion: Nor of the
Queen of *Sheba*, whose Journey to hear the Wisdom
of *Solomon*, shews her own good Judgment and great
Share in that excellent Endowment. *Solomon* does
not think himself too wise to be instructed by his
Mother, nor too great to record her Lessons, which,
if he had followed, he might have spared the Trouble
of Repentance, and been delivered from a great deal
of that Vanity he so deeply regrets.

WHAT Reason can be assign'd why the Mothers
of the Kings of *Judah*, are so frequently noted in
those very short Accounts that are given of their
Reigns, but the great Respect paid them, or perhaps
their Influence on the Government, and Share in the

Administration? This is not improbable, since the wicked *Athaliah* had Power to carry on her Intrigues so far as to get Possession of the Throne, and to keep it for some Years. Neither was there any Necessity for *Asa*'s removing his Mother (or Grandmother) from being Queen, if this were merely Titular, and did not carry Power and Authority along with it. And we find what Influence *Jezabel* had in *Israel*, indeed to her Husband's and her own Destruction.

It was a *Widow-Woman* whom GOD made choice of to sustain his Prophet *Elijah* at *Zarephah*. And the History of the *Shunamite* is a noble Instance of the Account that is made of Women in Holy Scripture. For whether it was not the Custom in *Shunem* for the Husband to dictate, or whether her's was conscious of her superior Vertue, or whatever was the Reason, we find it is she who governs, *dwelling* with great Honour and Satisfaction *among her own People*. Which Happiness she understood so well, and was so far from a troublesome Ambition, that she desires no Recommendation to *the King or Captain of the Host*, when the Prophet offer'd it, being already greater than they could make her. The Text calls her a *Great Woman*, whilst her Husband is hardly taken Notice of, and this, no otherwise, than as performing the Office of a Bailiff. It is *her* Piety and Hospitality that are Recorded, *She* invites the Prophet to *her House;* who converses with, and is entertained by *her*. She gives her Husband no Account of *her* Affairs any further, than to tell him *her* Designs, that he may see them executed. And when he desires to know the Reason of her Conduct, all the Answer she affords is, *Well*, or, as the Margin has it from the *Hebrew, Peace*. Nor can this be thought assuming, since it is no more than what the Prophet encourages, for all his Addresses are to *her*, he takes no Notice of her Husband. His Benefits are conferr'd on *her*, 'tis *she* and *her Household* whom he warns of a Famine, and 'tis *she* who Appeals to the King for the Restitution of *her House* and *Land*. I would not infer from hence, that Women, generally speaking, ought to govern in their Families when they have a Husband; but I think this Instance and Example is a sufficient Proof, that if by Custom or Contract, or the Laws of the Country, or Birth-right, (as in the Case of Sovereign Princesses) they have the supreme Authority, it is no Usurpation, nor do they act contrary to Holy Scripture, nor consequently to the Law of Nature. For they are no where, that I know of, forbidden to claim their just Right: The Apostle, 'tis true, would not have them *usurp* Authority, where Custom and the Law of the strongest had brought them into Subjection, as it has in these Parts of the World. Though in remoter Regions, if Travellers rightly inform us, the Succession to the Crown is intail'd on the Female Line.

GOD Himself, who is *no Respecter of Persons, with whom there is neither Bond nor Free, Male nor Female, but* they *are all one in Christ Jesus,* did not deny Women that Divine Gift the Spirit of Prophecy, neither under the *Jewish* nor Christian Dispensation. We have nam'd two great Prophetesses already, *Miriam* and *Deborah;* and besides other Instances, *Huldah* the Prophetess was such an Oracle, that the good King *Josiah,* that great Pattern of Vertue, sends even the High Priest himself to consult her, and to receive Directions from her in the most arduous Affairs. *It shall come to pass,* saith the Lord, *that I will pour out my Spirit upon all Flesh, and your Sons and your Daughters shall Prophesy,* which was accordingly fulfill'd by the Mission of the Holy *Ghost* on the Day of *Pentecost,* as St. *Peter* tells us. And, besides others, there is mention of four Daughters of *Philip,* Virgins, who did Prophesy. For, as in the *Old,* so in the *New Testament,* Women make a considerable Figure; the Holy Virgin receiving the greatest Honour that Human Nature is capable of, when the Son of GOD vouchsafed to be her Son, and to derive his Humanity from her only. And if it is a greater Blessing *to hear the Word of* GOD *and keep it*, who are more considerable for their Assiduity in this, than the Female Disciples of our LORD? *Mary* being Exemplary, and receiving a noble Encomium from Him, for her Choice of the better Part.

IT would be thought tedious to enumerate all the excellent Women mentioned in the *New Testament*, whose humble Penitence and ardent Love, as *Magdalen*'s; their lively Faith and holy Importunity, as the *Syrophenician*'s; extraordinary Piety and Uprightness, as *Elizabeth*'s; Hospitality, Charity and Diligence, as *Martha*'s, *Tabitha*'s, *&c.* (see St. *Luke* viii.); frequent and assiduous Devotions and Austerities, as *Anna*'s; Constancy and Courage, Perseverance and ardent Zeal, as that of the Holy Women who attended our LORD to His Cross, when His Disciples generally forsook, and the most Courageous had denied Him; are Recorded for our Example. Their Love was stronger than Death, it followed our Saviour into the Grave. And, as a Reward, both the Angel, and even the LORD Himself, appears first to them, and sends them to preach the great Article of the Resurrection to the very Apostles, who being, as yet, under the Power of the Prejudices of their Sex, esteem'd the Holy Womens *Words as idle Tales, and believed them not.*

SOME Men will have it, that the Reason of our LORD's appearing first to the Women, was, their being least able to keep a Secret; a witty and masculine Remark, and wonderfully Reverent! But not to dispute whether those Women were Blabs or no, there are many Instances in Holy Scripture, of Women who did not betray the Confidence repos'd in them. Thus *Rahab*, though formerly an ill Woman, being converted by the *Report* of those Miracles, which, though the *Israelites saw*, yet they *believed not in* GOD, *nor put their Trust in his Word*, She acknowledges the GOD of Heaven, and, as a Reward of her faithful Service in concealing *Joshua*'s Spies, is, with her Family, exempted from the Ruin of her Country, and also, has the Honour of being named in the *Messiah's* Genealogy. *Michal*, to save *David's* Life, exposes her self to the Fury of a Jealous and Tyrannical Prince. A Girl was trusted by *David*'s grave Counsellors to convey him Intelligence in his Son's Rebellion; and when a Lad had found it out, and blab'd it to *Absalom*, the King's Friends confiding in the Prudence and Fidelity of a Woman, were secur'd by her. When our LORD escaped from the *Jews*, he trusted Himself in the Hands of *Martha* and *Mary*. So does St. *Peter* with another *Mary*, when the Angel deliver'd him from *Herod,* the Damsel *Rhoda* too, was acquainted with the Secret. More might be said, but one would think here is enough to shew, that whatever other great and wise Reasons Men may have for despising Women, and keeping them in Ignorance and Slavery, it can't be from their having learnt to do so in Holy Scripture. The Bible is for, and not against us, and cannot without great Violence done to it, be urg'd to our Prejudice.

However, there are strong and prevalent Reasons which demonstrate the Superiority and Pre-eminence of the Men. For in the first Place, Boys have much Time and Pains, Care and Cost bestow'd on their Education, Girls have little or none. The former are early initiated in the Sciences, are made acquainted with antient and modern Discoveries, they study Books and Men, have all imaginable Encouragement; not only Fame, a dry Reward now a-days, but also Title, Authority, Power, and Riches themselves, which Purchase all Things, are the Reward of their Improvement. The latter are restrain'd, frown'd upon, and beat, nor *for*, but *from* the Muses; Laughter and Ridicule, that never-failing Scare-Crow, is set up to drive them from the Tree of Knowledge. But if, in spite of all Difficulties Nature prevails, and they can't be kept so ignorant as their Masters would have them, they are star'd upon as Monsters, censur'd, envied, and every way discouraged, or, at the best, they have the Fate the Proverb assigns them, *Vertue is prais'd and starv'd*. And therefore, since the coarsest Materials need the most Curing, as every Workman can inform you, and the worst Ground the most elaborate Culture, it undeniably follows, that Mens Understandings are superior to Womens, for, after many Years Study and Experience, they become wise and learned, and Women are not Born so!

AGAIN, Men are possessed of all Places of Power, Trust and Profit, they make Laws and exercise the Magistracy, not only the sharpest Sword, but even all the Swords and Blunderbusses are theirs, which by the strongest Logick in the World, gives them the best Title to every Thing they please to claim as their Prerogative: Who shall contend with them? Immemorial Prescription is on their Side in these Parts of the World, antient Tradition and modern Usage! Our Fathers, have all along, both taught and practised Superiority over the weaker Sex, and consequently Women are by Nature inferior to Men, as was to be demonstrated. An Argument which must be acknowledged unanswerable; for, as well as I love my Sex, I will not pretend a Reply to *such* Demon-stration!

ONLY let me beg to be inform'd, to whom we poor Fatherless Maids, and Widows who have lost their Masters, owe Subjection? It can't be to all Men in general, unless all Men were agreed to give the same Commands; Do we then fall as Strays, to the first who finds us? By the Maxims of some Men, and the Conduct of some Women one would think so. But whoever he be that thus happens to become our Master, if he allows us to be reasonable Creatures, and does not meerly Compliment us with that Title, since no Man denies our Readiness to use our Tongues, it would tend, I should think, to our Master's Advantage, and therefore he may please to be advis'd to teach us to improve our Reason. But if Reason is only allow'd us by way of Raillery, and the secret Maxim is, that we have none, or little more than Brutes, 'tis the best way to confine us with Chain and Block to the Chimney-Corner, which, probably, might save the Estates of some Families and the Honour of others.

I Do not propose this to prevent a Rebellion, for Women are not so well united as to form an Insur-rection. They are for the most part wise enough to love their Chains, and to discern how very becomingly they fit. They think as humbly of themselves as their Masters can wish, with respect to the other Sex, but in regard to their own, they have a Spice of Masculine Ambition; every one would Lead, and none would Follow. Both Sexes being too apt to Envy, and too backward in Emulating, and take more Delight in detracting from their Neighbour's Vertue, than in improving their own. And therefore, as to those Women who find themselves born for Slavery, and are so sensible of their own Meanness, as to conclude it impossible to attain to any thing excellent, since they are, or ought to be best acquainted with their own Strength and Genius, She's a Fool who would attempt their Deliverance or Improvement. No, let them enjoy the great Honour and Felicity of their tame, submissive and depending Temper! Let the Men applaud, and let them glory in this wonderful Humility! Let them receive the Flatteries and Grimaces of the other Sex, live unenvied by their own, and be as much belov'd as one such Woman can afford to love another! Let them enjoy the Glory of treading in the Footsteps of their Predecessors, and of having the Prudence to avoid that audacious Attempt of soaring beyond their Sphere! Let them Huswife or Play, Dress, and be pretty entertaining Company! Or, which is better, relieve the Poor to ease their own Compassions, read pious Books, say their Prayers, and go to Church, because they have been taught and us'd to do so, without being able to give a better Reason for their Faith and Practice! Let them not by any means aspire at being Women of Understanding, because no Man can endure a Woman of Superior Sense, or would treat a reasonable Woman civilly, but that he thinks he stands on higher Ground, and, that she is so wise as to make Exceptions in his Favour, and to take her Measures by his Directions; they may pretend to Sense, indeed, since meer Pretences only render one the more ridiculous! Let them, in short, be what is call'd *very* Women, for this is most acceptable to all sorts of Men; or let them aim at the Title of *good devout* Women, since some Men can bear with this; but let them not judge of the Sex by their own Scantling: For the great Author of Nature and Fountain of all Perfection, never design'd that the Mean and Imperfect, but that the most Compleat and Excellent of His Creatures in every Kind, should be the Standard to the rest.

To conclude; If that GREAT QUEEN who has subdued the Proud, and made the pretended Invincible more than once fly before her; who has Rescued an Empire, Reduced a Kingdom, Conquer'd Provinces in as little Time almost as one can Travel them, and seems to have chain'd Victory to her Standard; who disposes of Crowns, gives Laws and Liberty to *Europe*, and is the chief Instrument in the Hand of the Almighty, to pull down and to set up the great Men of the Earth; who conquers every where for others, and no where for her self but in the Hearts of the Conquer'd, who are of the Number of those who reap the Benefit of her Triumphs; whilst she only reaps for her self the Lawrels of disinterested Glory, and the Royal Pleasure of doing Heroically; if this Glory of her own Sex, and Envy of the other, will not think we need, or does not hold us worthy of, the Protection of her ever victorious Arms, and Men have not the Gratitude, for her sake at least, to do Justice to her Sex, who has been such a universal Benefactress to theirs: Adieu to the Liberties, not of this or that Nation or Reign only, but of the Moiety of Mankind! To all the great Things that Women might perform, inspir'd by her Example, encouraged by her Smiles, and supported by her Power! To their Discovery of new Worlds for the Exercise of her Goodness, new Sciences to publish her Fame, and reducing Nature it self to a Subjection to her Empire! To their destroying those worst of Tyrants Impiety and Immorality, which dare to stalk about even in her own Dominions, and to devour Souls almost within View of her Throne, leaving a Stench behind them scarce to be corrected even by the Incense of her Devotions! To the Women's tracing a new Path to Honor, in which none shall walk but such as scorn to Cringe in order to Rise, and who are Proof both against giving and receiving Flattery! In a Word, to those Halcyon, or, if you will, *Millennium* Days, in which the Wolf and the Lamb shall feed together, and a Tyrannous Domination, which Nature never meant, shall no longer render useless, if not hurtful, the Industry and Understandings of half Mankind!

## *FINIS.*